Advanced Diploma Synoptic

Workbook

Sheriden Amos

Published by Osborne Books Limited
Tel 01905 748071
Email books@osbornebooks.co.uk
Website www.osbornebooks.co.uk

Design by Laura Ingham

Printed by CPI Group (UK) Limited, Croydon, CR0 4YY, on environmentally friendly, acid-free paper from managed forests.

MIX
Paper from
responsible sources
FSC® C019777

British Library Cataloguing in Publication Data
A catalogue record for this book is available from the British Library

ISBN 978 1911198 086

Contents

Also available from Osborne Books...

Tutorials

Clear, explanatory books written
precisely to the specifications

Wise Guides

Handy pocket-sized study and revision guides

Student Zone

Login to access your free ebooks and
interactive revision crosswords

Download **Osborne Books App** free from the App Store or Google Play Store
to view your ebooks online or offline on your mobile or tablet.

www.osbornebooks.co.uk

Introduction

Qualifications covered

This book has been written specifically to cover the AAT Synoptic Assessment, which is mandatory for the following qualifications:

- AAT Advanced Diploma in Accounting – Level 3
- AAT Advanced Diploma in Accounting at SCQF Level 6

This book provides four full Practice Assessments to prepare students for the Computer-Based Synoptic Assessment. Further details of the content and structure of the book are shown on page 1.

Osborne Study and Revision Materials

Our materials are tailored to the needs of students studying this unit and revising for the assessment. They include:

- **Tutorials:** paperback books with practice activities
- **Wise Guides:** pocket-sized spiral bound revision cards
- **Student Zone:** access to Osborne Books online resources
- **Osborne Books App:** Osborne Books ebooks for mobiles and tablets

Visit www.osbornebooks.co.uk for details of study and revision resources and access to online material.

HOW TO USE THIS SYNOPTIC ASSESSMENT WORKBOOK

INTRODUCTION

The AAT Advanced Diploma in Accounting covers a range of complex accounting tasks, including maintaining cost accounting records and the preparation of reports and returns. It comprises the following five mandatory units:

- Advanced Bookkeeping *
- Final Accounts Preparation *
- Management Accounting: Costing *
- Ethics for Accountants
- Spreadsheets for Accounting

All of the units within this Advanced Diploma in Accounting are mandatory. Three units are assessed individually in end-of-unit assessments (in the bulleted list above these are indicated with an *). This qualification also includes a synoptic assessment that students sit towards the end of the qualification, which draws on and assesses knowledge and understanding from across all units in the qualification.

Students must successfully complete all three of the unit assessments and the synoptic assessment to achieve the qualification.

synoptic assessment coverage

Two of the units in this qualification are only assessed through the synoptic assessment. These are Ethics for Accountants and Spreadsheets for Accounting. However, the synoptic assessment for the Advanced Diploma in Accounting covers five of the mandatory units and has five assessment objectives (AO). These are detailed as follows:

AO1 Demonstrate an understanding of the relevance of the ethical code for accountants, the need to act ethically in a given situation and the appropriate action to take in reporting questionable behaviour.

AO2 Prepare accounting records and respond to errors, omissions and other concerns in accordance with accounting and ethical principles and relevant regulations.

AO3 Apply ethical and accounting principles when preparing final accounts for different types of organisation, develop ethical courses of action and communicate relevant information effectively.

AO4   Use relevant spreadsheet skills to analyse, interpret and report management accounting data.

AO5   Prepare financial accounting information, comprising extended trial balances and final accounts for sole traders and partnerships, using spreadsheets.

synoptic assessment structure

The synoptic assessment for the Advanced Diploma in Accounting is a computer-based assessment that is partially computer-marked and partially human-marked. The live synoptic assessment is a total of three hours with 75 minutes for Section One and 105 minutes for Section Two. Unused time cannot be transferred between sections and once you have completed Section One and moved on to Section Two you will not be able to go back.

task instructions for section two

Section Two tasks are based on amending or producing data in a spreadsheet package. The instructions for each task in Section Two of the Practice Synoptic Assessments are included within this book. In the exam, the instructions for each task will be on the first worksheet of the spreadsheet data for that task. The spreadsheet data on the Osborne Books website only includes the data, not the instructions. You will need to look at the AAT Sample Assessments to ensure you are familiar with where the task instructions can be found for Section Two before you take the exam.

what this book contains

This book provides four full Practice Synoptic Assessments to prepare students for the live Computer-Based Synoptic Assessment. They are based directly on the structure, style and content of the sample assessment material provided by the AAT at www.aat.org.uk. In order to complete Section Two of these Practice Synoptic Assessments you will need to download files from the Osborne Books website and work in a spreadsheet software program. Access to these files can be gained through the 'Products and Resources' button on the menu bar and then via the 'Advanced Diploma Synoptic Workbook' book page.

The AAT sample assessment material provides a breakdown of the marks allocated to each task. This helps students to appreciate the relative importance of each task in the assessment and to plan how long to spend on each task. The Practice Synoptic Assessments in this book also show the mark allocation for each task.

Suggested answers to the Practice Synoptic Assessments are set out in this book.

The AAT recommend that students complete all other assessments before attempting the synoptic assessment and there are restrictions in place to prevent premature scheduling of the synoptic assessment. It is suggested that in order to gain maximum benefit from this book students should not attempt these Practice Synoptic Assessments until they have studied all five units and completed the three unit assessments.

Practice
synoptic
assessment 1

assessment information

Read the scenario carefully before attempting the questions.

Complete all 5 tasks.

Tasks 1.1 to 1.3 in Section 1 require you to write your answers in this book.

Tasks 2.1 to 2.2 in Section 2 require you to download files and work outside the assessment environment in a spreadsheet software program. The files are available, as indicated, on the Osborne Books website.

You should ensure that you save all your files prior to finishing and marking this assessment.

advice

Read each question carefully before you start to answer it.

Attempt all questions.

You will have 3 hours to answer all parts of the assessment.

Note: Important information for the live assessment:

In the live assessment you will have 75 minutes to complete Section 1 and 105 minutes to complete Section 2. Any used time will not be transferable between Sections. For example, if you complete Section 1 in 60 minutes, you will still have 105 minutes to complete Section 2.

You will not be able to go back and review Section 1 once you have finished it, so double check your answers before you leave Section 1!

scenario background

You are Jo Bradley, a part-qualified accountant who works at First Class Flooring, a partnership making and selling wooden flooring to retailers. The partners, George Walker and Janek Bach have worked together for many years.

You are responsible for all aspects of accounting and bookkeeping.

Section 1

For all Tasks except 1.1

Scenario background

You are Jo Bradley, a part-qualified accountant who works at First Class Flooring, a partnership making and selling wooden flooring to retailers. The partners, George Walker and Janek Bach have worked together for many years.

You are responsible for all aspects of accounting and bookkeeping.

Task 1.1: 15 marks

This task is based on a different workplace scenario to the rest of the assessment.

Bill is an accountant who works for Artons Limited, a large business with a large number of employees. He has just employed Sarah, a part-qualified accountant.

Sarah has been discussing her understanding of the Code of Ethics with Bill.

(a) Are the following statements true or false?

Statement	True	False
'I will not have to keep so up to date with the latest accounting regulations once I have qualified'		
'I am never allowed to share information I have learned through my job with anyone else'		

(2 marks)

(b) Show whether the ethical code requires Sarah to take the following actions in order to act in line with the principle of professional behaviour.

Action	Required	Not Required
Comply with all laws that affect Artons Limited		
Report misreporting of information by the Finance Director		

(2 marks)

(c) Sarah reported being sick one day last week and did not come to work. However, a colleague of Bill's saw her at a local event during that day, with a group of her friends.

Which fundamental principle has Sarah breached?

(a)	Integrity	
(b)	Professional competence and due care	
(c)	Objectivity	

(1 mark)

(d) When confronted with her breach, Sarah commented that the Sales Director was claiming for petrol on expenses for a car which is not his. Therefore she thought her behaviour was acceptable.

Indicate whether the following statements are true or false.

Statement	True	False
The Sales Director's behaviour indicates unethical leadership of the organisation		
The values and ethics of the Directors will influence the values and actions of staff		

(2 marks)

(e) Sarah has committed other ethical breaches and is now facing disciplinary action by Artons Limited.

State the action that each organisation below may take against Sarah.

The AAT | may / may not | expel Sarah from the AAT as a result of disciplinary procedures.

Artons Limited | may / may not | bring disciplinary procedures against Sarah.

The National Crime Agency | may / may not | bring disciplinary procedures against Sarah.

(3 marks)

(f) Syed is an accountant who works for Bodmin Limited reporting to Mo, who is also an accountant. Syed has discovered that Bodmin Limited have been illegally polluting a local stream with waste from their plant. Mo is aware of the pollution, as are the Directors, and has told Syed to ignore it.

What action must Syed now take?

(a)	Inform the directors of the pollution and say that it should stop	
(b)	Follow the internal procedures within Bodmin Limited for reporting unethical behaviour	
(c)	Ignore it	

(2 marks)

(g) Syed is considering 'whistleblowing' about the pollution to the Environment Agency.

Under what circumstances will Syed be protected from dismissal if he whistleblows?

Circumstance	Protected	Not protected
Syed believes the disclosure to be true		
Syed does not act in good faith		
Syed believes the evidence will be concealed or destroyed		

(3 marks)

Scenario Background (for Tasks 1.2 – 1.3)

You are Jo Bradley, a part qualified accountant who works at First Class Flooring, a partnership making and selling wooden flooring to retailers. The partners, George Walker and Janek Bach have worked together for many years.

You are responsible for all aspects of accounting and bookkeeping.

Task 1.2: 15 marks

This task is based on the workplace scenario for First Class Flooring.

Today's date is 15 September 20-9.

You have received an invoice from a supplier, for standard-rated goods, which you are checking.

From: Dean Timber Limited Advantage Business Village, Cinderford GL17 0BD	To: First Class Flooring Unit 15, Holwick Industrial Estate Holwick Loop Road Nottingham NG4 2AB	Invoice Date: 14 September 20-9	Invoice number: 206157
Purchase Order: 6543	Delivery Date: 7 September 20-9		
Description	**Quantity**	**Per Unit** £	£
Oak 2.4m x 100mm x 200mm	100	25.58	2,558.00
		VAT at standard rate	460.44
		Total	3,018.44
VAT Registration number 789 165 078			

(a) What is the correct amount of VAT which should be included on the invoice when it is posted into the day books?

£

(1 mark)

(b)   First Class Flooring's VAT account at 30 September 20-9, the end of its last VAT quarter, is as follows:

Date	Detail	£	Date	Detail	£
6 August	Cash book	43,890.21	01 July	Balance b/d	43,890.21
30 Sept	Purchases day book	70,714.28	30 Sept	Sales day book	115,383.33
30 Sept	Sales returns day book	1,696.13	30 Sept	Purchases returns day book	781.86
30 Sept	Balance c/d	43,754.78			
		160,055.40			160,055.40

On reviewing First Class Flooring's day books, you have found two errors:

- Input VAT of £1,215.67 on a purchase invoice was wrongly recorded as rent expenses on 15 August.

- A supplier understated input VAT on an invoice received by £130 and posted to the ledgers by First Class Flooring on 29 September.

You prepare the journals and correct the errors. Once the journals have been processed, what will be the revised balance carried down on the VAT account?

£

(2 marks)

You discover that in the last three months, the Sales Clerk at First Class Flooring, Janet Moran, has raised several invoices for flooring for two employees and has not included any VAT on the sales. This means that the VAT is understated by a significant amount. When you go to discuss the issue with her, she states that she 'thought sales to employees were not VATable' and will 'tell the partners that you told her to treat the sales this way for VAT purposes' as she does not want to lose her job.

(c)   Which ethical principles are being broken by Janet Moran? Tick **all** that apply.

(a) Professional competence and due care	
(b) Professional behaviour	
(c) Confidentiality	

(2 marks)

You investigate further and find out that the employees who purchased the flooring were both related to Janet Moran. You now consider it to be deliberate.

(d)   Applying the conceptual framework from the ethical code, which of the following describes the situation faced by Janet Moran when charging VAT on sales to relatives?

(a) A familiarity threat to objectivity	
(b) A self review threat to integrity	
(c) An intimidation threat to professional competence and due care	

(2 marks)

(e) What action should you take?

(a) Send a Suspicious Activity Report to the National Crime Agency	
(b) Tell George and Janek about your concerns	

(1 mark)

(f) Enter each of the figures below into the appropriate place in the statement of profit or loss. You are told products are priced to give a gross profit margin of 20%. Closing inventory equals 30% of the month's sales.

116,856   23,371   93,485   85,548   −35,057

Statement of profit or loss for the period ended 30 September

	£	£
Sales revenue		
Opening inventory		
Purchases		
Less closing inventory		
Cost of sales		
Gross profit		

(3 marks)

(g) Calculate the missing figure for opening inventory.

£ [   ]

(1 mark)

(h) Which **one** of the following will have been accounted for in the **purchases figure?**

(a) Purchase returns	
(b) Discounts received	
(c) Discounts allowed	

(1 mark)

(i) Complete the following statement for allowance for doubtful debts.

When the allowance for doubtful debts is increased, there will | always / sometimes / never | be a negative effect on profit.

(2 marks)

Task 1.3: 15 marks

George and Janek have recently reviewed the service provided by the payroll bureau and have decided to set up an internal payroll in First Class Flooring. They have asked you to find a suitable package and look at running the payroll within the next two months. They have offered you a substantial pay rise for performing these additional duties. You have no experience of payroll but you were hoping for a pay rise as you are in the process of buying your first house.

(a)   Describe **two** threats to your ethical principles.

(2 marks)

(b)   Describe **two** actions you could take to remain ethical.

(2 marks)

(c)   You have been asked by George and Janek to consider how they could make the business more sustainable.

Give **one** reason why sustainability would be important to First Class Flooring.

(1 mark)

(d)   George Walker has sent you the following email:

EMAIL

To: Jo Bradley
From: George Walker
Date: 1 December 20-9
Subject: Re – Final Accounts

Hi Jo,

I am looking to invest in some new equipment and the bank have asked for a set of accounts, 'produced on the usual going concern basis' and I have no idea what they mean! Could you explain the following:

(1)   What is a going concern? Why is it important?

(2)   Why should the accounts be produced on this basis? How would they be different if the going concern concept was not used?

(3)   Could we send the bank the management accounts, instead of the final year end figures and if not, why not?

Many thanks

George

Write an email to George explaining the points raised in the above email.

EMAIL

To: George Walker
From: Jo Bradley
Date: 3 December 20-9
Subject: Re – Going Concern and Final Accounts

(10 marks)

Section 2

For Tasks 2.1 – 2.2

Scenario background

You are Jo Bradley, a part-qualified accountant who works at First Class Flooring, a partnership making and selling wooden flooring to retailers. The partners, George Walker and Janek Bach have worked together for many years.

You are responsible for all aspects of accounting and bookkeeping.

Task 2.1: 25 marks

Today's date is 1 April 20-9.

George and Janek have asked you to prepare some volume analysis for them, as they are looking at how much profit they could make in the next quarter at different levels of output.

Download the spreadsheet file 'Practice Assessment 1 Task 2.1 data.xlsx' from the Osborne Books website.

Save the spreadsheet file in an appropriate location and rename it using the following format: 'your initial-surname-AAT no-dd.mm.yy-Task 2.1'. For example: J-Bradley-123456-12.03.xx-Task 2.1.

A high degree of accuracy is required. You must save your work as an .XLS or .XLSX file at regular intervals to avoid losing your work.

You are to compare the profitability of First Class Flooring for different levels of output for the next quarter to 30 June 20-9.

(a) • Open this renamed file. In the worksheet called 'Output Analysis', reformat all text in this sheet to be Calibri.

 • Use 'copy' and 'paste values' (not paste-link) to insert the figures from the worksheet 'Budget' column C into the correct positions in the Current Budget column (column G) of the 'Output Analysis' worksheet.

 • Insert a row underneath Row 3.

 • Enter 'Percentage of Current Budget' in A4.

 • In F4, G4, H4 and I4 calculate the % of each output vs 'Current Budget'.

 • Format the cell % to two decimal places.

 • Calculate the budget for each output for the revenue and each cost, using absolute referencing where necessary.

(12 marks)

(b) In the 'Output Analysis' worksheet:

 • Format the costs and revenues to £0,000.

 • Make sure all column headings in rows 2-4 are in bold.

 • Calculate the operating profit for each level of output in row 16 and show profit as a positive figure and losses as a negative figure.

 • Perform a spell check and ensure all contents can be seen.

(6 marks)

(c)
- Copy the range A3-I3, showing column headings, into a new worksheet, keeping the formatting the same. Name this worksheet 'Values'.
- Copy the range A7-I15 and paste only the formatting and values.
- Produce subtotals for each of: materials, direct labour, variable overheads and fixed overheads.
- Show subtotals in Scenario 1, Current Budget, Scenario 2, and Scenario 3 columns.
- Hide the detail to only show the subtotals and grand total, not the individual components.

(4 marks)

George and Janek have been told by the bank that their target profit for next year must be £45,000. George wants to know how much the cost of Direct materials 2 needs to be reduced in the Current Budget in order to meet this target profit.

(d) To answer George's question, you will need to use the Goal Seek function. You must capture evidence of this in the worksheet called 'Screen Print' before accepting the Goal Seek answer.

- Copy all the data in the 'Output Analysis' worksheet and paste (not paste-link) it into the 'Goal Seek' worksheet, starting in cell A1.
- In the 'Goal Seek' worksheet use the Goal Seek function to investigate what change in Direct materials 2 cost figure (cell G8) would be required to generate an actual operating profit of £45,000 in cell G16.
- When the completed Goal Seek dialog box is showing – but BEFORE you click the OK button – use the print screen function to capture the evidence of your work and then accept the Goal Seek.
- In the 'Screen Print' worksheet, paste the screenshot.

(3 marks)

At the end of this task you should have one spreadsheet (saved as an .XLS or .XLSX file) to upload to your computer with the following five worksheets: 'Budget', 'Output Analysis', 'Goal Seek', 'Screen Print' and 'Values'.

Task 2.2: 30 marks

Today's date is 30 April 20-9.

First Class Flooring has suffered a computer crash. You have been asked to complete the quarterly sales spreadsheet for the three months ended 31 March 20-9 which was extracted immediately before the crash.

Download the spreadsheet file 'Practice Assessment 1 Task 2.2 data.xlsx' from the Osborne Books website.

Save the spreadsheet file in the appropriate location and rename it using the following format: 'your initial-surname-AAT no-dd.mm.yy-Task 2.2'. For example: J-Bradley-123456-12.03.xx-Task 2.2.

A high degree of accuracy is required. You must save your work as an .XLS or .XLSX file at regular intervals to avoid losing your work.

(a)   Open this renamed file, open the worksheet called 'Invoices'.

  • Check for and remove any duplicates in the invoices.

  • If there were any duplicates, enter the number found in cell H1.

  • Use a lookup function on the 'Item No' data to calculate the net sales using information from the Price List worksheet.

  • Use absolute referencing to calculate the gross sales value of each invoice using the VAT figure provided in cell G1.

(4 marks)

(b)   In the 'Invoices' worksheet:

  • Freeze the panel for columns A to D and set up filters on the whole table. Filter net sales, using the number filter to show the top ten net sales.

  • Insert a subtotal formula in the net sales column to work out the average of the top ten sales.

  • Format the numerical data in the net and gross invoice columns to GBP currency (£0.00).

  • Set the worksheet to show formulas (rather than the resulting values of the formulas) and ensure all the contents can be seen when you set page to landscape.

  • Take a screenshot of the worksheet showing formulas and paste it into a new worksheet in your current workbook.

  • Name this new worksheet 'Screen Print'.

  • Return to the Invoices worksheet and remove the 'Show formulas' setting.

(5 marks)

(c) Insert a pivot chart and pivot table into a new worksheet of the net value of 'Senza Natural' flooring sold in each of the three months from January to March. Name this worksheet 'Senza Natural Net Sales'

  - Ensure the pivot table is sorted in chronological month order.

  - Format the chart series to show highest sales for the period in green and lowest sales in black.

  - Add a chart title 'Senza Natural Net Sales'.

  - Enlarge the chart so that the whole legend is clearly seen.

  - Produce a trend line and colour it green.

(6 marks)

You are now preparing the final accounts for First Class Flooring for the year ended 31 December 20-8.

The statement of profit or loss for First Class Flooring shows a profit for the year ended 31 December 20-8 of £159,950.

The business is still operated as a partnership.

You are given the following information:

  - George is entitled to a salary of £20,000 per annum. Janek earns no salary.

  - Over the year George has earned commission of £3,877 and Janek has earned commission of £3,743.

  - George has taken drawings of £56,200 over the year, and Janek has taken £62,200.

  - Interest on drawings has been calculated at £600 for George and £720 for Janek for the year ended 31 December 20-8.

  - The residual profit after adjustments is shared between George and Janek in the ratio 2:3.

You are required to prepare the appropriation account and current accounts for First Class Flooring for the year ended 31 December 20-8.

(d) Using formulas where appropriate, complete the partnership appropriation statement and current accounts in the 'First Class Flooring 1' spreadsheet to appropriate the profit for the year ended 31 December 20-8 between the two partners in accordance with the partnership agreement, by making the appropriate entries from the data given above.

(15 marks)

At the end of this task you should have one spreadsheet (saved as an .XLS or .XLSX file) to upload to the assessment environment with the following five worksheets: 'Senza Natural Net Sales', 'Invoices', 'Price List', 'Screen Print' and 'First Class Flooring 1'.

Practice synoptic assessment 2

assessment information

Read the scenario carefully before attempting the questions.

Complete all 5 tasks.

Tasks 1.1 to 1.3 in Section 1 require you to write your answers in this book.

Tasks 2.1 to 2.2 in Section 2 require you to download files and work outside the assessment environment in a spreadsheet software program. The files are available, as indicated, on the Osborne Books website.

You should ensure that you save all your files prior to finishing and marking this assessment.

advice

Read each question carefully before you start to answer it.

Attempt all questions.

You will have 3 hours to answer all parts of the assessment.

Note: Important information for the live assessment:

In the live assessment you will have 75 minutes to complete Section 1 and 105 minutes to complete Section 2. Any used time will not be transferable between Sections. For example, if you complete Section 1 in 60 minutes, you will still have 105 minutes to complete Section 2.

You will not be able to go back and review Section 1 once you have finished it, so double check your answers before you leave Section 1!

scenario background

This scenario applies to Tasks 1.2 to 2.2. It does not apply to Task 1.1.

You are Tim Oakley, a part qualified accountant who bookkeeps for Amy Cox, a sole trader. She runs Catering for Occasions, a catering business, which has been operating for many years.

You are responsible for all aspects of accounting and bookkeeping.

Section 1

For all Tasks except 1.1

Scenario background

You are Tim Oakley, a part-qualified accountant who bookkeeps for Amy Cox, a sole trader. She runs Catering for Occasions, a catering business, which has been operating for many years.

You are responsible for all aspects of accounting and bookkeeping.

Task 1.1: 15 marks

This task is based on a workplace scenario separate to the rest of the assessment.

Alek is an accountant who works in practice at Able and Best, a medium-sized accountancy practice. A client recently made the following statements to him, stating her beliefs on Alek's duties as an AAT member.

(a) Are these statements true or false?

Statement	True	False
You have to do whatever I tell you in my accounts, as I am your client		
You have to keep to rules, which tell you how to behave ethically in every situation		

(2 marks)

(b) In the following situations, identify whether Alek does or does not comply with the principle of objectivity.

Situation	Comply	Not Comply
Alek produced the financial statements for his sister-in-law's business		
Alek accepts a meal for his family for free from a local client who owns a restaurant		

(2 marks)

(c) Alek's colleague, Monica, stated to Mr Able, one of the partners, that she had completed a tax return for a client, Rushwick and Co, when she had not.

Which fundamental ethical principle did Monica breach?

(a) Confidentiality	
(b) Integrity	
(c) Objectivity	

(1 mark)

(d) Alek provides bookkeeping services, including raising invoices, to People First, a small recruitment agency. The business has a March year end. The owners have asked Alek to date several invoices as April, when the sales occurred in March, to reduce the tax bill for this year.

What should Alek do? Tick **all** that apply.

Action	Tick to do
Agree with the client and record the accounts in April	
Inform his manager	
Document the request on People First's file	
Report People First to the National Crime Agency (NCA)	

(3 marks)

(e) Fruity Fruits Limited, a local fruit farm, is using Able and Best to process its payroll. It pays the National Minimum Wage to its pickers and charges them significantly above market rent to live in caravans on site.

Which of the following statements are true?

Statement	True	False
By paying the National Minimum Wage, Fruity Fruits is acting ethically		
Charging high rents to the pickers raises doubts about Fruity Fruits Limited's ethical approach to business		

(2 marks)

(f) Alek has been given a new client and has discovered they are improperly accounting for VAT and so underpaying VAT to HMRC. He has spoken to them and suggested they disclose the error immediately. They have refused to do so.

What does Alek need to do next? Tick **all** that apply.

Action	
(a) Tell the client he will be reporting them to HMRC	
(b) Make a Suspicious Activity Report to the Money Laundering Reporting Officer	

(2 marks)

(g) Alek has now inadvertently become involved in money laundering with a client, Patios and Paving. Complete the following statement.

If Alek informs Patios and Paving he is going to report them for | money laundering / tax evasion | he will be guilty of | tipping off / whistle blowing | and will be | covered under protected disclosure / | liable to be prosecuted | .

(3 marks)

> **Scenario Background (for Tasks 1.2 – 1.3)**
>
> You are Tim Oakley, a part-qualified accountant who bookkeeps for Amy Cox, a sole trader. She runs Catering for Occasions, a catering business, which has been operating for many years.
>
> You are responsible for all aspects of accounting and bookkeeping.

Task 1.2: 15 marks

You have been reviewing Amy's expenses for the year and have realised that she has claimed VAT on entertaining several important regular corporate clients last quarter. The entertaining amount claimed is £1,260, including VAT.

(a)   What will the journal be to correct this error?

Select the General ledger code from the following: Entertaining, VAT control a/c, Bank, Drawings

General ledger code	Dr £	Cr £

(2 marks)

(b)   As a result of the adjustment in part (a), what will the impact on the profit for the year be?

Choose **one** option.

(a)	Increase the profit	
(b)	Decrease the profit	
(c)	No change to the profit	

(1 mark)

Amy Cox has been approached by a client, Ted, who has suggested he pay Amy in cash. He suggested no invoice be raised for his birthday party, so he could pay a lower price and he would save the VAT. He also pointed out that Amy will save the tax on the profit.

Amy has told your colleague, Sarah, who also works in accounts, that she intends to do this and has promised to share the saving in tax with her.

(c)   Applying the ethical framework from the ethical code, which of the following describes the situation faced by Sarah? Choose **one** option.

(a) A self-review threat to objectivity	
(b) An intimidation threat to objectivity	
(c) A self-interest threat to objectivity	

(2 marks)

You conclude that the deliberate misrecording of sales is unethical behaviour by Sarah.

(d)   What should your action be regarding Sarah?

(a) Send a suspicious Activity Report to the National Crime Agency	
(b) Discuss the situation with Sarah and try to persuade her to report the sale correctly	

(1 mark)

Amy is looking at expanding into providing a bar service as part of her business. She has suggested that you look into the matter for her with a view to helping her work through the paperwork and applying for the licence, as you are good at rules and regulations. She thinks she will be licensed within two months and wants to offer it as a service to her clients now.

(e)   What action should you take?

(a) Resign from Catering for Occasions	
(b) Agree to help her but suggest she does not advertise it yet	
(c) Decline the work and suggest she contact a local specialist in licence applications	

(2 marks)

You are working through the trial balance and have a suspense account balance of £350 cr. You have found the following errors, which you must correct:

- Payment of a miscellaneous food invoice for £172 posted as a credit to the bank, with no corresponding debit.

- The equipment balance is shown correctly on the general ledger as £5,545 but has been transferred to the trial balance as £5,145.

(f)   What is the balance on the suspense account once these adjustments have been made? Complete the amount and choose Dr or Cr.

 Dr / Cr

(2 marks)

(g)   If corrected, what error could now clear the suspense account?

(a) A wages payment made using petty cash which did not have a petty cash slip produced for it	
(b) A sundry sale made through petty cash, with no petty cash slip created for it	

(1 mark)

As part of the year end procedures you are completing the bank reconciliation as at 31 December 20-4. You have compared the cash book and the bank statement found the following issues:

(h)   Which **two** of the following items require the cash book to be updated?

(a) A faster payment of £375 has been recorded in the cash book as £275	
(b) A cheque paid to a supplier for £500 has cleared the bank on 5 January 20-5	
(c) Overdraft charges of £57 have not been entered into the cash book	
(d) A customer remittance was received dated 30 December 20-4, which has been entered into the cash book. The receipt has not yet been received	

(2 marks)

(i)   Amy is unclear why you reconcile the bank account to the cash book every month.

Choose **one** reason.

(a)	To keep track of the bank balance each period	
(b)	To make sure the bank is applying the correct bank charges	
(c)	To ensure the cash book accurately reflects the bank transactions of the business	

(2 marks)

Task 1.3: 15 marks

When Amy is catering for events, she employs waiting staff to serve at the event. Waiting staff are all casually employed and you process the payroll for them. You have discovered during your work that Amy is including tips given to waiting staff as part of their minimum wage, which is incorrect. Without these, the staff would be earning below minimum wage.

You have discussed this with Amy and she stated that the staff wages were a very high proportion of her costs and she would reduce her profits significantly if she were to pay them more. She has suggested that the business would not continue to trade if she had to change the wage rates.

(a)   Explain the **two** threats to ethical principles that you face.

(2 marks)

(b)   Explain the actions you must now take, including any information you must record and any advice you might seek.

(2 marks)

(c)   Amy has asked you to help promote and uphold sustainability in Catering for Occasions.

State why, as an accountant, you have a professional duty to uphold sustainability as part of your role.

(1 mark)

Amy Cox is considering trading as a limited company but is unsure what this means and how it will affect the way she runs the business.

(d)   Write an email to Amy covering the following areas:

   (1)   State the ownership and reporting requirements of each type of business

   (2)   Explain the accounts regulations covering a sole trader and a limited company

   (3)   State one advantage of becoming a limited company

EMAIL

To: Amy Cox

From: Tim Oakley

Date: 12 January 20-5

Subject: Sole Trader or Limited Company

(10 marks)

Section 2

For Tasks 2.1 – 2.2

Scenario background

You are Tim Oakley, a part-qualified accounting technician. You provide bookkeeping services for Catering for Occasions, owned by Amy Cox, a business which provides catering services.

You cover all aspects of bookkeeping and accounting for the business.

Task 2.1: 25 marks

The date is 31 January 20-5.

Luke Graham has asked you to prepare some management accounts information for him, analysing the year's performance against budget.

Download the spreadsheet file 'Practice Assessment 2 Task 2.1 data.xlsx' from the Osborne Books website.

(a)
- Open this file. In the worksheet called 'Variance analysis' insert 'Catering for Occasions' in cell A1 in bold, Font size 11. Insert 'Year ended 31 December 20-4' in cell A2, in the same format.
- Ensure all data can be viewed.
- Spell check the information on the 'Variance analysis' spreadsheet.
- In cell C3 enter '£' and copy across to E3.
- Use 'copy' and 'paste link' to insert the figures from the worksheet 'Budget and actual data' columns C and D into the correct positions in columns C and D of the 'Variance analysis' worksheet.
- Format all text to be in Times New Roman.

(4 marks)

(b)
- Insert a row underneath Row 2. Insert another row under Row 4.
- Enter '% of Budget' in F4. Merge and centre cells E2 and F2.
- Format the column F to % to two decimal places.
- Calculate the £ variance for each item of revenue and each cost, for cells E6-E16. Use conditional formatting to show favourable variances in black and adverse variances in red, as a '–' (minus) figure.
- Calculate the variance % of budget in cells F6-F16.
- Format the budget and actual figures to 0,000.
- Calculate the operating profit for the budget and actual results and variance value. Put this information in row 17.

(9 marks)

(c) • Put an IF statement in E18 to show 'Balanced' if the variance £ column total equals E17 and 'check' if it does not.

• Insert a header 'Catering for Occasions Year ended 31 December 20-4'.

• Insert a footer to show 'Variance analysis' current time, date and page number.

(5 marks)

(d) • Copy the range A2-D10 and paste only the values into a new worksheet, keeping the formatting the same. Name this worksheet 'Food and drink analysis'.

• In the newly created worksheet called 'Food and drink analysis', change the description from 'cooking staff' to 'Food'.

• Change the costs to '–' (minus) figures. Data sort the table into product types, with food at the top.

• In cell A10 insert 'Food margin' and then calculate the food gross margin to go into cells C10 and D10. Repeat this for row 11 for drinks. Format the cells C10-D11 into percentage to two decimal places.

• Ensure Rows 10 and 11 are in Times New Roman font and text can be read.

(4 marks)

Amy has asked you to help her produce a month by month sales budget for next year, 20-5. She believes she can achieve an overall sales budget of £130,000. She would like to break this down for each month, using last year's sales pattern, as the business is very seasonal.

(e) You will need to use the data on the 'Forecast 20-5' worksheet.

• Enter the budgeted sales level for 20-5 into cell B2.

• Complete the '% of total of 20-4' information in cells C6-C17, using a formula to calculate each month. You will need to use absolute referencing of the total sales for 20-4, cell B18.

• Apply the calculated percentage for each month to the budgeted level of sales for 20-5, with reference to cell B2 to complete 'Target 20-5' (column D).

• Enter a total formula in cells C18 and D18.

• Show formulas in the worksheet and use the screen print to copy this.

• In the 'Screen Print' worksheet, paste the screenshot.

• Change the 'Forecast 20-5' worksheet back to show the numbers.

(3 marks)

At the end of this task you should have one spreadsheet (saved as an .XLS or .XLSX file) to upload to your computer with the following five worksheets: 'Budget and actual data', 'Variance analysis', 'Food and drink analysis', 'Forecast 20-5' and 'Screen Print'.

Task 2.2: 30 marks

Today's date is 1 February 20-6.

You have been given a spreadsheet containing data of the employees and their hours of work for January. Amy has asked you to do some analysis on the data for her.

Download the spreadsheet file 'Practice Assessment 2 Task 2.2 data.xlsx' from the Osborne Books website.

Save the spreadsheet file in an appropriate location and rename it using the following format: 'your initial-surname-AAT no-dd.mm.yy-Task 2.2'. For example: T-Oakley-123456-12.03.xx-Task 2.2.

A high degree of accuracy is required. You must save your work as an .XLS or .XLSX file at regular intervals to avoid losing your work.

(a)   Open this renamed file. In the worksheet called 'January Working' use a lookup function on the 'Person name' data to fill in column E with the wage rate for the person, using information from the 'Wage rate' worksheet. Retitle the column 'Wage rate'.

   •   Check for and remove any duplicates in the wages.

   •   If there were any duplicates, enter the number found in cell H1.

   •   Use column F to calculate the Wage rate multiplied by Hours to give the 'Gross Wages'.

   •   Format the 'Wage rate' and 'Gross Wages' columns for £0.00.

   •   Make sure all the contents of every cell can be seen.

(4 marks)

(b)   Use the subtotal function to total the wages cost of each job. Hide the detail. Copy and paste this information into a new worksheet called 'Analysis wages by job'.

   •   Hide the data for columns C-E.

   •   Insert a 2D pie chart showing the wages bill for January by job. Resize it so the key is clearly visible.

   •   Insert a title above the chart 'Analysis of January wages by job'.

   •   Format the 'Smith wedding total' on the chart to show yellow and the 'Zuckerman birthday total' to show pink.

   •   Change the chart to include the % of the total wages for each job.

(7 marks)

(c)   Go to the 'Job Analysis' worksheet

- Link the subtotals for each job from the 'Analysis wages by job' to the wages cell in column G.

- Format the sheet as 0,000.00.

- Insert total formulas for each column.

- Set the worksheet to show formulas (rather than the resulting values of the formulas) and ensure all the contents can be seen when you set page to landscape.

- Take a screenshot of the worksheet showing formulas and paste it into the 'Screen Print' worksheet in your current workbook.

- Return to the Job Analysis worksheet and remove the 'Show formulas' setting.

(3 marks)

You are now preparing the final accounts for Catering for Occasions for the year ended 31 December 20-5.

You are using a spreadsheet that you have input the ledger balances into, which creates the financial statements. So far you have input the ledger balances only and have completed no other work.

You also have the following information:

- Closing inventory value is £3,097, which has not been included in the accounts yet.

- Depreciation on the van for the year has not been included yet of £3,600.

- Included within insurance is a bill of £800 which covers the period 1 July 20-5 to 30 June 20-6.

- A bill for £452 relating to 1 October to 31 December for electricity has not yet been accrued.

You are required to prepare the extended trial balance and financial statements for Catering for Occasions for the year ended 31 December 20-5.

(d)   Using the 'Extended Trial Balance' worksheet:

- Format all headings to have bold size 11 font for columns E-L.

- Merge and centre for each of the Statement of profit or loss and the Statement of financial position headings. Wrap text for each of these headings and adjust Row 2 to ensure the text can be seen.

- Using a formula, extend the trial balance balances across to the correct place in the Statement of profit or loss and the Statement of financial position columns, including the 'Adjustments' column.

- Use an IF statement to ensure the debits and credits in each set of Dr and Cr columns balance, showing the difference if they do not balance and 'OK' if they do.

(6 marks)

(e) Input the adjustments to the extended trial balance to complete the figures. Add a row in for Accruals or Prepayments as required. Include a narrative underneath the trial balance showing your working for:

- The adjustment to the insurance in cell C37

- The depreciation in cell C38

- The electricity accrual in cell C39

Enter the closing inventory figure for both the Statement of profit or loss and the Statement of financial position.

Enter the profit figure for the year, which is correctly calculated to be £18,121, into the extended trial balance as appropriate. Check all Dr and Cr columns balance.

(4 marks)

(f) Go to the 'Financial statements' worksheet:

- Update the Statement of financial position to include prepayments, by inserting a line into the spreadsheet below Trade receivables.

- Update the Statement of financial position to include accruals, by inserting a line into the spreadsheet below Trade payables.

- Link the closing inventory from the 'Extended trial balance' to the correct place in the Financial Statements, correcting the Cost of Sales calculation.

- Using the relevant spreadsheet skills and your accounting knowledge, find out how to correct the current assets formula. Before making the correction and removing the arrows, use Print Screen to take a screen shot of the financial statements sheet and save it on to the 'Current assets formula' worksheet.

- Compare the profit for the year on the Statement of profit or loss to that on the extended trial balance. Insert an IF statement to show 'Balanced' or the difference underneath the profit figure in the Statement of profit or loss into cell K33.

- Set up the document to print each statement in portrait, setting appropriate page breaks.

(6 marks)

At the end of this task you should have one spreadsheet (saved as an .XLS or .XLSX file) to upload to the assessment environment. This should have eight worksheets titled 'January working', 'Wage rate', 'Analysis wages by job', 'Job analysis', 'Screen Print', 'Extended trial balance', 'Financial statements' and 'Current assets formula', with information and data in them.

Practice synoptic assessment 3

assessment information

Read the scenario carefully before attempting the questions.

Complete all 5 tasks.

Tasks 1.1 to 1.3 in Section 1 require you to write your answers in this book.

Tasks 2.1 to 2.2 in Section 2 require you to download files and work outside the assessment environment in a spreadsheet software program. The files are available, as indicated, on the Osborne Books website.

You should ensure that you save all your files prior to finishing and marking this assessment.

advice

Read each question carefully before you start to answer it.

Attempt all questions.

You will have 3 hours to answer all parts of the assessment.

Note: Important information for the live assessment:

In the live assessment you will have 75 minutes to complete Section 1 and 105 minutes to complete Section 2. Any used time will not be transferable between Sections. For example, if you complete Section 1 in 60 minutes, you will still have 105 minutes to complete Section 2.

You will not be able to go back and review Section 1 once you have finished it, so double check your answers before you leave Section 1!

scenario background

This scenario applies to Tasks 1.2 to 2.2. It does not apply to Task 1.1.

You are Serena Parry, a part-qualified accountant who works for Beautiful Tableware, a partnership owned by Claire Giles and Jason Taylor, which has been operating for many years and produces stoneware dishes for cooking and serving food in.

You are responsible for all aspects of accounting and bookkeeping.

Section 1

Scenario background

For all Tasks except 1.1

You are Serena Parry, a part-qualified accountant who works for Beautiful Tableware, a partnership owned by Claire Giles and Jason Taylor, which has been operating for many years and produces stoneware dishes for cooking and serving food in.

You are responsible for all aspects of accounting and bookkeeping.

Task 1.1: 15 marks

This task is based on a workplace scenario separate to the rest of the assessment.

Daisy is an accountant who works in practice at Martin, Plum and Holsworth, a medium-sized accountancy practice. A new employee, Brian, has asked Daisy to clarify his understanding of the Code of Ethics.

(a)   Are these statements true or false?

Statement	True	False
How I behave in my personal life is not important to the AAT, as I only need to comply with the Code of Ethics at work		
If I have an ethical problem, I need to use a methodical approach to resolve it		

(2 marks)

(b)   In the following situations, identify whether Daisy does or does not comply with the principle of professional competence and due care.

Situation	Comply	Not Comply
Daisy completes the VAT return for a client who sells and buys overseas, when she has no experience of imports and exports		
Daisy attends a training course on new International Accounting Standards		

(2 marks)

(c)   Daisy has accepted two tickets to a show in London, plus a night in a hotel, from one of her clients, as a 'thank you' on completion of their accounts.

Which fundamental ethical principle did Daisy breach?

(a) Objectivity	
(b) Professional behaviour	
(c) Integrity	

(1 mark)

(d)   A few months ago, Daisy went to work for a client, Fantastic Floors Limited, to help them while the Financial Controller was on maternity leave. Whilst there, she set up a new asset register, calculating the depreciation and deciding on the useful lives of various new additions. She is due to work on the year end accounts and part of her work will be to review the asset register.

What ethical threat is Daisy facing to her objectivity?

(a) A self-interest threat	
(b) A familiarity threat	
(c) A self-review threat	

(1 mark)

What actions should Daisy take to safeguard against this threat? Tick **any** that could apply.

Action	Tick to do
Inform the client	
Complete the work, then inform her manager once the accounts are finished	
Inform her manager and request he reviews the work in detail once she has performed it	
Request to be removed from the work for this year end	

(3 marks)

(e) Daisy has noticed that one of her clients is making large payments to an overseas bank account with no supporting documentation. Daisy is concerned these may be payments to fund terrorism.

What action must Daisy take? Tick **all** that apply.

Action	
(a) Immediately inform Martin, Plum and Holsworth's Money Laundering Officer of her concerns	
(b) Complete a Suspicious Activity Report (SAR) and send it to the National Crime Agency (NCA)	

(2 marks)

(f) Daisy was working on the most recent corporation tax return for Excellence in Recruitment and noticed that they had incorrectly deducted entertaining expenditure on last year's return.

What action should Daisy take? Tick **one** option.

Action	
Correct the error on this year's return and do not tell anyone	
Advise HMRC of the error without disclosing it to Excellence in Recruitment or Martin, Plum and Holsworth	
Tell Martin, Plum and Holsworth of the error and recommend the error be disclosed to Excellence in Recruitment	

(2 marks)

(g) Daisy realises she has inadvertently become involved in a money laundering operation for Prestigious Presents Limited.

Complete the following statement:

If Daisy does not tell the MRLO of their money laundering she will be guilty of an unauthorised disclosure / failure to disclose / prejudicing an inquiry and could be imprisoned for up to five / fourteen years .

(2 marks)

> **Scenario background**
>
> **For Tasks 1.2 – 1.3**
>
> You are Serena Parry, a part-qualified accountant who works for Beautiful Tableware, a partnership owned by Claire Giles and Jason Taylor, which has been operating for many years and produces stoneware dishes for cooking and serving food in.
>
> You are responsible for all aspects of accounting and bookkeeping.

Task 1.2: 15 marks

(a) Whilst reviewing the non-current asset register you realise that a new lorry, included in vehicles, has been included on the non-current asset register and general ledger for £36,000, including the VAT. VAT is reclaimable on lorries.

What will the journal be to correct this error?

Select the General ledger code from the following: Vehicles, equipment, Cost, VAT control a/c, vehicles expenses

General ledger code	Dr £	Cr £

(2 marks)

(b) As a result of the adjustment in part (a), what will the impact on the depreciation charge for the year be?

Choose **one** option.

(a)	Increase the depreciation charge	
(b)	Decrease the depreciation charge	
(c)	No change to the depreciation charge	

(1 mark)

Jason and Claire have been reviewing their suppliers recently and plan to reduce them. They believe this will enable them to build better long-term relationships and give them more price stability. As a result of this, several suppliers are competing to supply the glazing used to finish the stoneware. Your colleague, Daniel Juke, a part-qualified accountant, has been part of the review, and is assessing the glazing suppliers.

You overheard Daniel on the phone yesterday, discussing a trip to see one supplier, Gorgeous Glazing Limited, in Bath. He will stay overnight and will go to a very expensive restaurant for dinner.

(c) Applying the conceptual framework, from the ethical code, which of the following describes the situation faced by Daniel Juke? Choose **one** option.

(a) A familiarity threat to professional behaviour	
(b) A self-interest threat to objectivity	
(c) A self-review threat to professional competence and due care	

(2 marks)

You have also now found out that he has emailed another supplier's tender to Gorgeous Glazing Limited. You conclude that this is unethical behaviour by Daniel Juke.

(d) What should you do now? Choose **one** option.

(a) Tell Jason and Claire about your concerns	
(b) Report Daniel to the AAT	

(1 mark)

As a result of Daniel's unethical behaviour, he has been dismissed. You are temporarily Beautiful Tableware's only accountant. There is a meeting planned with the bank this afternoon, to finalise a new overdraft facility, which Daniel Juke was negotiating. It is quite complex and you do not believe you are in a position to contribute fully to the meeting. Claire and Jason insist you are present and that the overdraft be signed.

(e) Which of the following should be your next action? Choose **one** option.

(a) Request that the visit from the bank be postponed	
(b) Agree to deal with the bank, in line with Claire and Jason's instruction	
(c) Phone the bank and discuss the problem with them	

(2 marks)

As a result of Daniel's dismissal, you have been asked to update the asset register for the following disposal. Claire bought a car on 1 April 20-2 for £17,500. It has been depreciated at 25% using the diminishing balance method. The company policy is to charge a full year's depreciation in the year of disposal. The car was sold on 1 January 20-5 for £5,000.

(f) How much is the depreciation on the car when it is sold?

(2 marks)

(g) How much is the profit on disposal?

(1 mark)

(h) Claire and Jason have asked you why the car is depreciated using the reducing balance method.

Which **one** of the following explanations would be suitable?

(a) So the carrying value always equals market value	
(b) To minimise the likelihood of a profit occurring when it is sold	
(c) To apply the accruals concept, matching cost to revenue	

(2 marks)

Claire and Jason are considering how to fund the purchase of a car for one of the salesmen. Beautiful Tableware is very profitable but they do not want to use current monies to fund the purchase.

(i) Which **one** of the following funding methods would you suggest they consider?

(a) Cash purchase		
(b) Purchase on 30 days' credit terms		
(c) Bank overdraft		
(d) Hire purchase		

(2 marks)

Task 1.3: 15 marks

Claire has been reviewing the year end figures you recently produced for the partners. She wants to move house next year and requires the profits she earns to be above a certain level, to secure the mortgage she needs. As the profit is currently too low, she has asked you to move some expenses into the next year, to increase the profit.

She has told you that Jason is aware of this request and is happy for you to do it. She has offered you a free set of their complete product range to say 'thank you'. The products are very expensive.

(a)   Explain the situation you face, with reference to the Code of Ethics, and state the **two** threats you face.

(3 marks)

(b)   Set out the actions you must now take, considering both Claire and Jason, to resolve this ethical conflict.

(2 marks)

(c)   Claire and Jason have been discussing setting up a charity, to send simple earthenware pots to India. However, they are not familiar with charities so would like some information on them.

Prepare an email to them setting out:

(1)   A brief description of a charity

(2)   Details of ownership and how the charity is structured and managed

(3)   Liability and taxation

(4)   The regulations that govern a charity

EMAIL

To: Claire Giles; Jason Taylor

From: Serena Parry

Date: 6 April 20-5

Subject: Charity information

(10 marks)

Section 2

Scenario background

For Tasks 2.1 – 2.2

You are Serena Parry, a part-qualified accounting technician. You work for Beautiful Tableware, a partnership owned by Claire Giles and Jason Taylor. It has been operating for many years and produces stoneware dishes for cooking and serving food in.

You are responsible for all aspects of accounting and bookkeeping.

Task 2.1: 25 marks

Today's date is 27 March 20-5.

You have started work on the overhead absorption rates for next year and were interrupted before you had time to finish them. You have collected the raw data and costs in a spreadsheet and are now ready to complete it.

Download the spreadsheet file 'Practice Assessment 3 Task 2.1 data.xlsx' from the Osborne Books website.

Save the spreadsheet file in an appropriate location and rename it using the following format: 'your initial-surname-AAT no-dd.mm.yy-Task 2.1'. For example: S-Parry-123456-12.03.xx-Task 2.1.

A high degree of accuracy is required. You must save your work as an .XLS or .XLSX file at regular intervals to avoid losing your work.

(a)   Open this renamed file. In the worksheet called 'Apportionment calculation' use a vlookup for values for the basis of apportionment in the table from F6 to K10. The basis of apportionment information is on the worksheet 'Basis of apportionment'.

  •   Apportion the total costs in the 'Apportionment £' table, using an appropriate formula and the data from the 'Apportionment basis' table.

  •   Use autosum to add the allocated costs across into cells K15 to K25.

  •   Put an 'IF statement' in L15 to compare total cost in E15 to the calculated cost in K15, showing 'OK' if correct and 'Error' if not. Copy this down to L19.

(10 marks)

(b)   You have been given the following information regarding the time spent by stores and maintenance:

	% of department time		
	Moulding	**Glazing**	**Finishing**
Stores	60	30	10
Maintenance	75	15	10

Complete the apportionment process using the direct method, apportioning the stores and maintenance costs using this information.

(5 marks)

(c)   The overheads are to be apportioned on machine hours for moulding and glazing, and labour hours for finishing.

	Moulding	**Glazing**	**Finishing**
Machine hours	25,100	3,865	200
Labour hours	1,300	750	1,232

On the 'Apportionment calculation' worksheet enter the Overhead Absorption Rate (OAR) for the correct department in F27, G27 and H27.

Format the cost information to GBP £0,000.00. Amend the columns to ensure the descriptions and data can be viewed. Make the title of the 'Apportionment £' table bold. Hide column E. Ensure all remaining information can be seen.

(7 marks)

(d)   Claire and Jason are concerned that the cost figures used for rent and rates and the supervisors' salaries may be too low. They want you to revise the absorption rates based on these being an additional 10% higher. You must capture evidence of this in the worksheet called 'Screen print'.

- Copy all the data in the 'Apportionment calculation' worksheet and use paste (not paste-link) into the 'Revised apportionment' worksheet, starting in cell A1.

- Amend the columns, so all descriptions and numbers can be read.

- Amend the rent and rates figure to be 10% higher, using a formula to increase the figure in cell E18.

- Amend the supervisors' salaries figure to be 10% higher, using a formula to increase the figure in cell E19.

- Use 'Show formulas' to show the formulas and use the print screen function to capture evidence of this change.

- In the 'Screen print' worksheet, paste the screenshot.

- Go back to 'Revised apportionment' and show the numbers.

(3 marks)

At the end of this task you should have one spreadsheet (saved as an .XLS or .XLSX file) to upload to your computer with the following four worksheets: 'Apportionment calculation', 'Basis of apportionment', 'Revised apportionment' and 'Screen print'.

Task 2.2: 30 marks

Today's date is 1 June 20-5.

You have been given a spreadsheet containing data of March's sales. Claire and Jason have asked you to do some analysis on it.

Download the spreadsheet file 'Practice Assessment 3 Task 2.2 data.xlsx' from the Osborne Books website.

Save the spreadsheet file in an appropriate location and rename it using the following format: 'your initial-surname-AAT no-dd.mm.yy-Task 2.2'. For example: S-Parry-123456-12.03.xx-Task 2.2.

A high degree of accuracy is required. You must save your work as an .XLS or .XLSX file at regular intervals to avoid losing your work.

(a)   Open this renamed file. In the worksheet called 'Stoneware sales March' use an absolute reference to calculate the 'Net sales' value for each transaction in column F. Input 'Net amount' into cell F2.

- Ensure all the data is visible and resize column B so it fits the data. Double the row size for row 2.

- Wrap text in cells E2 and F2. Format columns E and F to show GBP currency £0,000.00.

- In box H2, count the total number of transactions, using the Count formula.

- Insert a comment stating 'Number of sales made in March' into box H2.

- Filter the table from smallest to largest net value of sales. Insert a formula to show the average of the highest 5 sales in cell F180. Enter the text 'Average of highest five sales' in G180 in bold font and italics.

- Copy and paste the worksheet into the 'Formulas' worksheet and set the sheet to show formulas.

(8 marks)

(b)   •   Insert a pivot table and pivot column chart into a new worksheet of the 'gross amount' of 'Traditional' range of stoneware sold for each colour.

- Ensure the pivot table is in alphabetical colour order.

- Format the chart series so that the lowest gross sales colour is in red and the highest is in green.

- Add a chart title 'Traditional Range Sales'.

- Name this worksheet 'Traditional Range Sales'.

- Set the page to print out on landscape, fitting on one page.

- Save as a pdf file called 'Practice Assessment 3 Task 2.2 Traditional Sales Range Chart'.

(8 marks)

The final accounts for Beautiful Tableware for the year ended 31 March 20-5 show Claire's capital account as £35,000 and Jason's capital account as £25,000. Neither partner has any transactions on these accounts in the current year. Claire and Jason currently share profits in the ratio 3:2 respectively.

They have asked their friend Andrea Summerwell to enter the partnership and the goodwill in the business has been valued at £48,000. Andrea will bring £45,000 of cash into the business as her capital, part of which represents a premium for goodwill. She paid them through the bank on 1 April 20-5. The new profit sharing ratio for Claire, Jason and Andrea will be 3:2:3 respectively.

Claire and Jason have asked you to prepare a statement of their capital accounts, reflecting this change.

You are required to prepare the capital statement for Beautiful Tableware as at 1 April 20-5.

(c)   Complete the partnership capital statement on the 'Capital account' tab for the partners.

(8 marks)

(d)   One part of the Partnership Agreement states that Claire and Jason will earn commission on sales, with minimum monthly sales and percentages to be agreed yearly. Next year, if they make sales in excess of £8,000 per month, they will earn 5% of all sales. They have asked you to look back at last year's sales data on the forecast sales commission worksheet and forecast their commission based on this data.

- Format all headings to have bold size 11 font.

- Merge and centre 'Sales' and 'Commission' over their respective columns.

- Spell check the data.

- Use a custom list to sort the whole table from January to December.

- Use an IF statement to calculate the commission on sales for Claire and Jason for each month, using cells B1 and B2 within it and absolute referencing. Show your results in columns D and E.

- Total each of the columns B:E.

- In the shaded area, format the range B7:E19 in GBP currency with the thousand separator and two decimal places (e.g. £3,200.00).

(4 marks)

Claire wants to know the commission rate she would need to earn £7,000.

(e)   Amend your spreadsheet to show this:

- Open a new worksheet and name it 'Goal seek'.

- Return to the 'Forecast sales commission' worksheet. Use What if Goal Seek analysis to amend your data.

- When the completed Goal Seek dialog box is showing – but BEFORE you click the OK button – take a screenshot (without pasting). Then complete the Goal Seek analysis.

- Return to the 'Goal seek' worksheet and paste the screenshot.

(2 marks)

At the end of this task you should have one spreadsheet (saved as an .XLS or .XLSX file) to upload to your computer with the following six worksheets: 'Traditional Range Sales', 'Stoneware sales March', 'Formulas', 'Capital account', 'Forecast sales commission' and 'Goal seek'. You should also have one pdf file called 'Practice Assessment 3 Task 2.2 Traditional sales range chart'.

Practice synoptic assessment 4

assessment information

Read the scenario carefully before attempting the questions.

Complete all 5 tasks.

Tasks 1.1 to 1.3 in Section 1 require you to write your answers in this book.

Tasks 2.1 to 2.2 in Section 2 require you to download files and work outside the assessment environment in a spreadsheet software program. The files are available, as indicated, on the Osborne Books website.

You should ensure that you save all your files prior to finishing and marking this assessment.

advice

Read each question carefully before you start to answer it.

Attempt all questions.

You will have 3 hours to answer all parts of the assessment.

Note: Important information for the live assessment:

In the live assessment you will have 75 minutes to complete Section 1 and 105 minutes to complete Section 2. Any used time will not be transferable between Sections. For example, if you complete Section 1 in 60 minutes, you will still have 105 minutes to complete Section 2.

You will not be able to go back and review Section 1 once you have finished it, so double check your answers before you leave Section 1!

scenario

This scenario applies to Tasks 1.2 to 2.2. It does not apply to Task 1.1.

You are Bruno Costa, a part-qualified accountant who works for Luke Graham, a sole trader, who runs Trendy Togs, a clothing business, which has been operating for a couple of years.

You are responsible for all aspects of accounting and bookkeeping.

Section 1

Scenario background

For all Tasks except 1.1

You are Bruno Costa, a part-qualified accountant who works for Luke Graham, a sole trader, who runs Trendy Togs, a clothing business, which has been operating for a couple of years.

You are responsible for all aspects of accounting and bookkeeping.

Task 1.1: 15 marks

This task is based on a workplace scenario separate to the rest of the assessment.

Paul is an accountant who works in Galvanised Products Limited, a manufacturing business employing many employees. A new employee, Edyta, needs help understanding the Code of Ethics and has asked Paul to help her.

(a)   Are these statements Edyta makes true or false?

Statement	True	False
Galvanised Products Limited's reputation may be damaged if I do not comply with the Code of Ethics		
The Code of Ethics sets out the rules I must apply in my work and personal life		

(2 marks)

(b)   In the following situations, identify whether Edyta does or does not comply with the principle of integrity.

Situation	Comply	Not Comply
Edyta informs her manager she is sick, when she is, in fact, going away for a long weekend		
Edyta made an error on payroll. She knows the incorrect information is included in the monthly reporting		

(2 marks)

(c) The sales bonuses are based on paying a fixed percentage of sales made for the month to each sales manager. Historically these have been displayed in the sales office. Edyta has been told by the Financial Controller, Emma, to increase the percentage for two of the four sales managers and to stop displaying the sales totals and bonuses. Edyta has no supporting documentation to support the change.

What fundamental ethical principle did Emma breach?

(a)	Integrity	
(b)	Objectivity	
(c)	Confidentiality	

(1 mark)

(d) Paul is due to be paid a bonus if reported profits are above a certain level. He is aware that a key customer is now unlikely to pay a debt and should provide for it, and profit would therefore be below the level for the bonus.

What threat to Paul's objectivity exists?

(a)	A self-review threat	
(b)	A self-interest threat	
(c)	A familiarity threat	

(1 mark)

What actions should Paul take to safeguard against this threat? Tick **any** that could apply.

Action	Tick to do
Request the Finance Director review the provision for bad and doubtful debts	
Follow the provisioning policy, as set out by the Finance Director	
Request to be removed from the work for this year end	

(3 marks)

(e)   Paul has found out that, as part of the production process, some health and safety regulations are being breached.

What action must Paul take? Tick **one** option.

Action	
(a) Discuss the matter with the management of Galvanised Products Limited and request they comply with the health and safety regulations	
(b) Resign	
(c) Report Galvanised Products Limited to the Health and Safety Executive immediately	

(2 marks)

(f)   During his work, Paul has discovered the Purchasing Director is being given sums of money to award contracts to a specific supplier.

What action should Paul take? Tick **one** option.

Action	
(a) Tell the Purchasing Director to stop	
(b) Inform the Managing Director of the Purchasing Director's actions	

(2 marks)

(g)   Paul has subsequently found out that the Managing Director is also taking bribes from several suppliers. He has been told by the Managing Director that he must 'keep quiet' or will lose his job.

Complete the following statement:

Paul must seek advice │ from a colleague / by phoning the AAT's Confidential helpline │ to determine

what to do next. If he believes the directors will destroy evidence of the bribes, he must make

│ a protected disclosure / an unprotected disclosure │ to the relevant authority.

(2 marks)

Scenario background

For Tasks 1.2 – 1.3

You are Bruno Costa, a part-qualified accountant who works for Luke Graham, a sole trader, who runs Trendy Togs, a clothing business, which has been operating for a couple of years.

You are responsible for all aspects of accounting and bookkeeping.

Task 1.2: 15 marks

As you are reviewing a supplier's account, you realise the VAT on a credit note they sent you shows VAT of £85.00 when it should have been £58.00. Currently the VAT control account includes debit balances totalling £2,135 and credit balances totalling £7,535.

(a) The amended amount on the VAT control account will be

(2 marks)

(b) Complete the following statement:

The VAT amount will be | due to / due from | HMRC.

(1 mark)

Luke has asked you why items under £250, such as clothes hangers, are not included in the non-current assets register.

(c) Choose **one** of the following options to explain why this is the case.

(a)	Luke has not asked you to do this. You will include all items from now on	
(b)	The principle of materiality means that the users' view of the accounts will not change if small items, such as clothes hangers, are not capitalised	
(c)	It is not worth the time and effort to maintain so many items on the non-current asset register	

(1 mark)

Luke Graham has noticed you spend a lot of time reconciling information for the accounts at the end of the month and this means Luke gets information later than he would like. He has asked you why you need to perform so many reconciliations at the end of the month.

(d)   Considering the underlying principles of producing accounts and the process of reconciliations, what explanation can you give him? Choose **one** option.

(a) The financial statements must be prepared on an accruals basis	
(b) The financial statements must be prepared on a going concern basis	
(c) The financial statements need to be free from material misstatement	

(2 marks)

You are now preparing the accruals and prepayments for the year ended 31 March 20-6. You have the following information for rent and vehicle costs for the year:

Rent

Rent prepaid 1 April 20-5	£1,750
Rent paid per bank during year	£8,470

A rent invoice for 1 March 20-6 to 31 May 20-6 of £3,090 is not included in the above figures.

Vehicle costs

Vehicle costs accrued 1 April 20-5	£500
Vehicle costs paid per bank during the year	£4,200

Included in the vehicle costs payments is the prepayment for road tax for 1 April – 31 March 20-7 of £256.

(e)   What is the profit and loss account charge for rent for the year?

(2 marks)

(f)   What is the profit and loss charge for vehicle costs for the year?

(2 marks)

Neil Clines is a builder and he is currently doing some building work for Luke Graham at his home. When you are reviewing the monthly management accounts, you identify an invoice for Neil Clines for building work. You are sure this is not a business purchase, but a personal one.

(g)   What action should you take?

(a)	Discuss this transaction with Luke Graham to find out if it is an error	
(b)	Report Luke Graham to HMRC	

(2 marks)

Luke is considering exporting clothes to America. He wants you to set up all the contracts and paperwork. You have no experience in this area.

(h)   What actions must you now take? Tick **all** that apply.

(a)	Explain that you have no experience of doing this to Luke and refuse to do it	
(b)	Suggest Luke discuss this with his accountant	
(c)	Contact the AAT helpline	

(3 marks)

Task 1.3: 15 marks

This task is based on the workplace scenario of Trendy Togs.

Today's date is 30 June 20-6.

Luke is considering reviewing the way he is dealing with his suppliers currently and has discussed it with you. He is planning to inform all the suppliers he will only use them if they give him an immediate 10% price reduction and accept extended payments terms of 60 days, rather than the current 30 days. He knows some suppliers will find it difficult to meet his request. They could experience cash flow and profitability problems as a result of it. His business is making profits and he has no cash flow issues.

He has suggested your fees could be increased if you help him persuade them that it would be in the best interests of the business. If you do not help, he has suggested he will find another bookkeeper.

(a) Identify and explain the sustainability issues regarding Luke's request.

(3 marks)

(b) Explain the **two** threats to ethical issues that you face as a result of Luke's request.

(2 marks)

(c) Identify what actions you can take to remain ethical in this situation.

(2 marks)

Luke is now considering asking a friend to invest some money into the business, so he can expand his product lines and increase sales. He has asked you to explain the difference between trading as a partnership and a sole trader.

(d) Write an email to Luke including:

(1) a description of a partnership and a sole trader

(2) the key differences between a partnership and a sole trader, including management, taxation and liability for debts

(3) one advantage and one disadvantage of operating as a partnership rather than a sole trader

---

EMAIL

To: Luke Graham

From: Bruno Costa

Date: 30 June 20-6

Subject: Partnership vs sole trader

(8 marks)

Section 2

Scenario background

For Tasks 2.1 – 2.2

You are Bruno Costa, a part-qualified accountant who works for Luke Graham, a sole trader, who runs Trendy Togs, a clothing business, which has been operating for a couple of years.

You are responsible for all aspects of accounting and bookkeeping.

Task 2.1: 25 marks

Today's date is 10 July 20-6.

Luke Graham is considering opening a shop and he has asked you to do some analysis for him. He would like you to determine what level of revenue he will need to break-even and make a profit. Luke has been given some cost information by a friend who owns a coffee shop, Coffee and Cake, in the same area he is looking to set up the shop, to help him.

You have been given a spreadsheet containing the Coffee and Cake cost data. You will need to adjust the data, in line with Luke's instructions, to create the break-even information for Trendy Togs' shop. Luke Graham has asked you to calculate the break-even revenue and how much he would have to sell to achieve a profit of £50,000. He works on a margin of 50% on all his clothes.

Download the spreadsheet file 'Practice Assessment 4 Task 2.1 data.xlsx' from the Osborne Books website.

Save the spreadsheet file in an appropriate location and rename it using the following format: 'your initial-surname-AAT no-dd.mm.yy-Task 2.1'. For example: B-Costa-123456-12.03.xx-Task 2.1.

A high degree of accuracy is required. You must save your work as an .XLS or .XLSX file at regular intervals to avoid losing your work.

(a) • Open this file. In the worksheet called 'Break-even analysis' insert 'Trendy Togs' in cell A1 in bold, Font size 12.

• Insert 'Break-even analysis new shop' in cell A2 in bold, font size 12.

• Spell check the text information on the 'Coffee and Cake data' spreadsheet then copy the information in A4-A12 over into the 'Break-even analysis' worksheet, starting at A5.

• Link the costs across from the 'Coffee and Cake data' worksheet into the 'Break-even analysis' worksheet using 'copy' and 'paste link' to the correct place in column B.

• Increase staff costs from 1.5 people to 2 people by amending the formula in cell B5. Amend the text to reflect this change.

• Increase 'Electricity' and 'Rates' by 5%.

• The depreciation will be £5000, based on Luke Graham's estimate.

• Increase 'Rent' and 'Insurance' by 10%.

• In cell B3 enter '£'.

• Use Autosum to fill in a total in B15.

• Format all text to be in Arial.

• Adjust width for column A so all text can be seen.

(11 marks)

(b) Complete the table underneath the cost information to show the Break-even revenue and the revenue needed for a profit of £50,000.

- Underneath the text 'Target profit' insert the amount £50,000 in cell C19.

- Link B21 and C21 to the total fixed costs from the working above.

- On the line for 'Revenue Required', use a formula to calculate the revenue assuming the margin of 50%.

- Insert a title 'Break-even analysis new shop' at the top of the table in cells A17-C17, using the text formatting in cell A2, merged and centred over the table.

- Ensure figures are formatted GBP £0,000.

(7 marks)

(c) Luke Graham has now asked you if he wished to earn £75,000 profit what the revenue would need to be.

- Insert a column between the Break-even and Target profit columns. Complete this column, to show the Target profit at £75,000. Insert 'Bonus' in cell C27.

- On the 'Break-even analysis' sheet, use 'show formulas', to show all formulas. Use print screen to copy and paste this to the worksheet called 'Screen print'. Go back to the 'Break-even analysis' sheet and remove 'show formulas'.

(4 marks)

(d) Luke has decided he would like to set up a bonus scheme for the staff. He will pay a bonus of 1.5% of sales for every £ of sales above the break-even revenue. He would like you to tell him how much the bonus will be at revenue levels £160,000, £300,000 and £400,000.

- In cell C29 enter an IF statement to calculate the amount of bonus payable at a revenue of £160,000. The bonus payment should equal 1.5% of sales above the break-even revenue amount, which has been calculated in cell B23. Use absolute referencing for the break-even revenue amount. Where no bonus is payable the IF statement should show 'No bonus'.

- Copy the IF statement in C29 into cells C30 and C31 to calculate the bonus payable at revenues of £300,000 and £400,000 respectively.

(3 marks)

At the end of this task you should have one spreadsheet (saved as an .XLS or .XLSX file) to upload to your computer with the following three worksheets: 'Coffee and cake data', 'Break-even analysis' and 'Screen print'.

Task 2.2: 30 marks

Today's date is 10 July 20-6.

At the end of June, the computer system suffered a crash. The data for April and May has now been reloaded back onto the system but the sales for June had a problem with the VAT and have not yet been reloaded.

You have been given a spreadsheet containing data of June's sales. Luke Graham has asked you to calculate the VAT on these sales for him. He also wants you to analyse the sales, looking at the type of products customers are buying.

Download the spreadsheet file 'Practice Assessment 4 Task 2.2 data.xlsx' from the Osborne Books website.

Save the spreadsheet file in an appropriate location and rename it using the following format: 'your initial-surname-AAT no-dd.mm.yy-Task 2.2'. For example: B-Costa-123456-12.03.xx-Task 2.2.

A high degree of accuracy is required. You must save your work as an .XLS or .XLSX file at regular intervals to avoid losing your work.

(a)   Open this renamed file. In the worksheet called 'Invoices' create a lookup table to complete the 'VAT rate' cell E5 on the 'Invoices' worksheet using the information from the 'VAT Information' worksheet. Use absolute referencing to allow you to complete this for all invoices. Make the VAT rate a percentage format. Input 'Net' into cell F4 then insert a formula to calculate the net amount in F5, and copy down the formula for all the invoices.

•   Ensure all the data is visible.

•   Remove duplicate items and record the number of duplicates in G1, highlighting the box green.

•   Format columns D and F to show GBP currency £0,000.00.

•   Sort the data in A5-F93 into Type order, A-Z.

(7 marks)

(b)   Insert a pivot table onto a new worksheet, including the fields 'customer', 'type' and 'net'.

•   Set the format for column B to £0,000.00.

•   Use the pivot table to show the sales for Andrews by type.

•   Insert a 3-D column chart.

•   Format the chart series so the children are in yellow, men in red and women in blue.

•   Add a chart title 'Sales to Andrews by Type'.

•   Name the worksheet 'Analysis Andrews'.

(4 marks)

(c) · Go back to the worksheet 'Invoices'.

· Insert text 'Maximum sales value' into cell B95 and use the maximum formula to complete cell F95.

· Insert text 'Minimum sales value' into cell B96 and use the minimum formula to complete cell F96.

(2 marks)

Today's date is 15 July 20-6.

You are now preparing the final accounts for Trendy Togs for the year ended 31 March 20-6.

You are using a spreadsheet to produce an extended trial balance. So far you have input the ledger balances only and have completed no other work.

You also have the following information:

· The current inventory valuation is £6,702.

· You need to set up an allowance for doubtful debts of 1% of the sales ledger.

· Depreciation figures of £2,000 for the van and £1,260 for the fittings have not yet been included.

· A box of inventory was incorrectly excluded when the closing inventory was initially valued. You need to value it appropriately and include it in the trial balance.

You are required to prepare the extended trial balance and financial statements for Trendy Togs for the year ended 31 March 20-6.

(d) Using the 'Extended Trial Balance' worksheet:

· Format all headings to have bold size 11 font.

· Merge and centre for each of the Statement of profit or loss and the Statement of financial position headings. Wrap text for each of these headings and increase the size of row 2 to make it visible.

· Use an IF statement underneath the total in every Cr column to ensure the debits and credits in each set of Dr and Cr columns balance, showing the difference if they do not balance and 'OK' if they do.

(4 marks)

(e)   Go to the 'Missing inventory information' worksheet.

- Sort the data into inventory number order.

- Insert an appropriate formula for each inventory item in the 'Inventory valuation worksheet', calculating the inventory value, based on IAS 2, where the item is valued at the lower of cost or net realisable value. Ensure it multiplies the quantity by the value.

- Put 'Total' in cell E18 and use the sum formula to calculate the inventory from the missing box in F18.

- Format cells D6 to F18 into £0,000.

- Use £0,000 format for cell F2.

- Format Boxes E18 and F18 using bold italic.

- Input a formula for the revised closing inventory valuation in F20, adding in the missing inventory. Format it as F2.

- Use show formulas to reveal the formulas on this worksheet. Screenshot the image and copy and paste it onto a new worksheet called 'Screen print'. Go back to worksheet 'Missing inventory valuation' and take off the 'show formulas' setting.

(6 marks)

(f)   Go back to the 'Extended Trial Balance Worksheet'. Freeze the top three rows.

Input the following adjustments to the extended trial balance in the adjustments column to complete the figures. Insert rows after row 28, as required to do this.

- The allowance for doubtful debts and the allowance for doubtful debts: adjustment. Use the round function to round it to the nearest £0.

- The depreciation.

- The closing inventory for both the Statement of profit or loss and the Statement of financial position, linking the value from the 'Missing inventory information' worksheet.

Enter the Profit / loss figure for the year into the extended trial balance, using a formula as appropriate. The profit calculated should equal £27,731. Insert a row underneath the 'Closing inventory Statement of financial position' line to do this. Check all Dr and Cr columns balance.

Using a formula, extend the trial balance balances across to the correct place in the Statement of profit or loss and the Statement of financial position columns.

(7 marks)

At the end of this task you should have one spreadsheet (saved as an .XLS or .XLSX file) to upload to the assessment environment. This should have six worksheets titled 'Analysis Andrews', 'Invoices', 'VAT Information', 'Extended Trial Balance', 'Missing inventory information' and 'Screen print' with information and data in them.

Answers to practice synoptic assessment 1

Section 1

Task 1.1: 15 marks

(a)

Statement	True	False
'I will not have to keep so up to date with the latest accounting regulations once I have qualified'		✔
'I am never allowed to share information I have learned through my job with anyone else'		✔

(b)

Action	Required	Not Required
Comply with all laws that affect Artons Limited	✔	
Report misreporting of information by the Finance Director	✔	

(c)   (a)   Integrity

(d)

Statement	True	False
The Sales Director's behaviour indicates unethical leadership of the organisation	✔	
The values and ethics of the Directors will influence the values and actions of staff	✔	

(e)   The AAT **may** expel Sarah from the AAT as a result of disciplinary procedures.

Artons Limited **may** bring disciplinary procedures against Sarah.

The National Crime Agency **may not** bring disciplinary procedures against Sarah.

(f)   (b)   Follow the internal procedures within Bodmin Limited for reporting unethical behaviour

(g)

Circumstance	Protected	Not protected
Syed believes the disclosure to be true	✔	
Syed does not act in good faith		✔
Syed believes the evidence will be concealed or destroyed	✔	

Task 1.2: 15 marks

(a)   £511.60

(b)   £43,754.78 – £1,215.67 – £130 = £42,409.11

(c)   (a)   Professional competence and due care
          (b)   Professional behaviour

(d)   (a)   A familiarity threat to objectivity

(e)   (b)   Tell George and Janek about your concerns

(f)   **Statement of profit or loss for the period ended 30 September**

	£	£
Sales revenue		116,856
Opening inventory		
Purchases	85,548	
Less closing inventory	–35,057	
Cost of sales	93,485	
Gross profit		23,371

(g)   £42,994

(h)   (a)   Purchase returns

(i)   When the allowance for doubtful debts is increased, there will **always** be a negative effect on profit.

Task 1.3: 15 marks

(a)   **Threat 1**

I do not have the appropriate experience to complete the payroll as it is a technical area, so I am not professionally competent to undertake it.

Threat 2

I am facing a self interest threat to my objectivity as I would like a pay rise to help run my new house.

(b)   **Action 1**

I would tell George and Janek that I do not have the relevant experience and need training to allow me to perform the task. This may take some time to organise.

Action 2

I could ask that their accountant undertake payroll, as they will have the appropriate knowledge.

(c)   It is important for First Class Flooring to take a long-term view, allowing it to meet the needs of the present generation without compromising those of a future generation.

(d)

EMAIL

To: George Walker

From: Jo Bradley

Date: 3 December 20-9

Subject: Re – Going Concern and Final Accounts

Dear George

Thank you for your email of 1 December 20-9.

Going concern and production of accounts

This is a fundamental principle when a set of accounts is prepared and it is the assumption that the business will continue to trade for the foreseeable future in its current form.

Assets and liabilities are recorded within the accounts when they are purchased or incurred. The method of valuation will assume that the business will run in its current format, so use the plant and machinery purchased over the course of several years, sell inventory at market rates and collect receivables fully.

If the business were to cease trading the value of these assets would have to be adjusted to reflect this. The plant and machinery would be valued at market value, not cost less depreciation. Inventory would all be valued at net realisable value.

If the business were to cease operating, additional liabilities could require recording eg redundancy payments.

Management account vs final accounts

The bank requires a final set of accounts, produced in a partnership format, so they can understand how the business is performing. The final accounts will include any adjustments, such as inventory losses or gains made on an inventory count, and will show a true picture of the financial position and profitability of the business.

Partnership accounts include similar information, so the bank can compare our business with others by using performance indicators and financial ratios, to see if we are well managed or not. As they wish to lend you money for the new equipment they will want to assess whether we will be able to repay the loan.

Please let me know if you need any further information.

Best wishes

Jo

Section 2

Task 2.1: 25 marks

(a) – (b)

	A	B	C	D	E	F	G	H	I	J
1										
2	**Levels of output**					**6000**	**7000**	**8000**	**10000**	
3	**Quarter ended 30 June 20x9**					**Scenario 1**	**Current Budget**	**Scenario 2**	**Scenario 3**	
4	**Percentage of Current Budget**					**85.71%**	**100.00%**	**114.29%**	**142.86%**	
5						£	£	£	£	
6	Revenue					£660,000	£770,000	£880,000	£1,100,000	
7	Materials:		Direct materials 1			£214,286	£250,000	£285,714	£357,143	
8	Materials:		Direct materials 2			£111,429	£130,000	£148,571	£185,714	
9	Direct labour:		Skilled			£42,000	£49,000	£56,000	£70,000	
10	Direct labour:		Unskilled			£60,000	£70,000	£80,000	£100,000	
11	Variable overheads:		Supervision			£27,429	£32,000	£36,571	£45,714	
12	Variable overheads:		Quality Control			£34,286	£40,000	£45,714	£57,143	
13	Variable overheads:		Production planning			£34,286	£40,000	£45,714	£57,143	
14	Fixed overheads:		Administration			£70,000	£70,000	£70,000	£70,000	
15	Fixed overheads:		Selling and distribution			£80,000	£80,000	£80,000	£80,000	
16	Operating Profit					-£13,714	£9,000	£31,714	£77,143	
17										

Budget / **Output Analysis** / Goal Seek / Screen Print / Values

(a) – (b) showing formulas

	A	B	C	D	E	F	G	H	I
1									
2	Levels of output					6000	7000	8000	10000
3	Quarter ended 30 June 20x9					Scenario 1	Current Budget	Scenario 2	Scenario 3
4	Percentage of Current Budget					=+F2/$G2	=+G2/$G2	=+H2/$G2	=+I2/$G2
5						£	£	£	£
6	Revenue					=G6*F$4	770000	=G6*H$4	=G6*I$4
7	Materials:		Direct materials 1			=G7*F$4	250000	=G7*H$4	=G7*I$4
8	Materials:		Direct materials 2			=G8*F$4	130000	=G8*H$4	=G8*I$4
9	Direct labour:		Skilled			=G9*F$4	49000	=G9*H$4	=G9*I$4
10	Direct labour:		Unskilled			=G10*F$4	70000	=G10*H$4	=G10*I$4
11	Variable overheads:		Supervision			=G11*F$4	32000	=G11*H$4	=G11*I$4
12	Variable overheads:		Quality Control			=G12*F$4	40000	=G12*H$4	=G12*I$4
13	Variable overheads:		Production planning			=G13*F$4	40000	=G13*H$4	=G13*I$4
14	Fixed overheads:		Administration			=G14	70000	=G14	=G14
15	Fixed overheads:		Selling and distribution			=G15	80000	=G15	=G15
16	Operating Profit					=F6-SUM(F7:F15)	=G6-SUM(G7:G15)	=H6-SUM(H7:H15)	=I6-SUM(I7:I15)
17									
18									
19									
20									

Budget   Output Analysis   Goal Seek   Screen Print   Values

(c)

1 2 3		A	B	C	D	E	F	G	H	I	J
	1	Quarter ended 30 June 20x9					Scenario 1	Current Budget	Scenario 2	Scenario 3	
+	4	Materials: Total					£325,714	£380,000	£434,286	£542,857	
+	7	Direct labour: Total					£102,000	£119,000	£136,000	£170,000	
+	11	Variable overheads: Total					£96,000	£112,000	£128,000	£160,000	
+	14	Fixed overheads: Total					£150,000	£150,000	£150,000	£150,000	
−	15	Grand Total					£673,714	£761,000	£848,286	£1,022,857	
	16										
	17										
	18										
	19										
	20										
	21										
	22										

Budget / Output Analysis / Goal Seek / Screen Print / **Values**

(d) Screen print of Goal Seek function

	A	B	C	D	E	F	G	H	I	J	K	L	M	N
1														
2	Levels of output					6000	7000	8000	10000					
3	Quarter ended 30 June 20x9					Scenario 1	Current Budget	Scenario 2	Scenario 3					
4	Percentage of Current Budget					85.71%	100.00%	114.29%	142.86%					
5						£	£	£	£					
6	Revenue					£660,000	£770,000	£880,000	£1,100,000					
7	Materials:	Direct materials 1				£214,286	£250,000	£285,714	£357,143					
8	Materials:	Direct materials 2				£111,429	£130,000	£148,571	£185,714					
9	Direct labour:	Skilled				£42,000	£49,000	£56,000	£70,000					
10	Direct labour:	Unskilled				£60,000	£70,000	£80,000	£100,000					
11	Variable overheads:	Supervision				£27,429	£32,000	£36,571	£45,714					
12	Variable overheads:	Quality Control				£34,286	£40,000	£45,714	£57,143					
13	Variable overheads:	Production planning				£34,286	£40,000	£45,714	£57,143					
14	Fixed overheads:	Administration				£70,000	£70,000	£70,000	£70,000					
15	Fixed overheads:	Selling and distribution				£80,000	£80,000	£80,000	£80,000					
16	Operating Profit					-£13,714	£9,000	£31,714	£77,143					
17														
18														

Goal Seek ? ×
Set cell: $G$16
To value: 45000
By changing cell: $G$8
OK   Cancel

Budget / Output Analysis / Goal Seek / **Screen Print** / Values

(d) Current Budget after Goal Seek

	A	B	C	D	E	F	G	H	I
1									
2	Levels of output					6000	7000	8000	10000
3	Quarter ended 30 June 20x9					Scenario 1	Current Budget	Scenario 2	Scenario 3
4	Percentage of Current Budget					85.71%	100.00%	114.29%	142.86%
5						£	£	£	£
6	Revenue					£660,000	£770,000	£880,000	£1,100,000
7	Materials:		Direct materials 1			£214,286	£250,000	£285,714	£357,143
8	Materials:		Direct materials 2			£80,571	£94,000	£107,429	£134,286
9	Direct labour:		Skilled			£42,000	£49,000	£56,000	£70,000
10	Direct labour:		Unskilled			£60,000	£70,000	£80,000	£100,000
11	Variable overheads:		Supervision			£27,429	£32,000	£36,571	£45,714
12	Variable overheads:		Quality Control			£34,286	£40,000	£45,714	£57,143
13	Variable overheads:		Production planning			£34,286	£40,000	£45,714	£57,143
14	Fixed overheads:		Administration			£70,000	£70,000	£70,000	£70,000
15	Fixed overheads:		Selling and distribution			£80,000	£80,000	£80,000	£80,000
16	Operating Profit					£17,143	£45,000	£72,857	£128,571
17									
18									
19									

Budget / Output Analysis / **Goal Seek** / Screen Print / Values

Task 2.2: 30 marks

(a) – (b)

	A	B	C	D	E	F	G	H	I	J
1					VAT					
2						20%				
3								3		
4	Name	Item	Finish	Description	Sold	When	Where	Invoice number	Net	Gross
35	Bravura Waxed	7894	Waxed	Prime Engineered Oak Brushed Waxed 15/4mm By 200mm By 1800-2200mm	49	January	Internet	14617	£5,390.00	£6,468.00
39	Bravura Waxed	7894	Waxed	Prime Engineered Oak Brushed Waxed 15/4mm By 200mm By 1800-2200mm	47	January	Wonderful Wood	14621	£5,170.00	£6,204.00
41	Dolce Natural	6814	Unfinished	Prime Engineered Oak Brushed Unfinished 15/4mm By 300mm By 1800-2500mm	49	January	Internet	14623	£5,145.00	£6,174.00
43	Dolce Natural	6814	Unfinished	Prime Engineered Oak Brushed Unfinished 15/4mm By 300mm By 1800-2500mm	49	January	Specialist Flooring	14625	£5,145.00	£6,174.00
52	Dolce Waxed	6815	Waxed	Prime Engineered Oak Brushed Waxed 15/4mm By 300mm By 1800-2500mm	46	January	Beautiful Homes	14634	£5,428.00	£6,513.60
84	Vivace Waxed	5989	Waxed	Superior Engineered Oak Brushed Waxed 20/6mm By 242mm By 2000-2350mm	49	January	Home Improvement	14666	£5,733.00	£6,879.60
131	Dolce Waxed	6815	Waxed	Prime Engineered Oak Brushed Waxed 15/4mm By 300mm By 1800-2500mm	48	February	Internet	14713	£5,664.00	£6,796.80
169	Vivace Waxed	5989	Waxed	Superior Engineered Oak Brushed Waxed 20/6mm By 242mm By 2000-2350mm	44	February	Specialist Flooring	14751	£5,148.00	£6,177.60
251	Vivace Waxed	5989	Waxed	Superior Engineered Oak Brushed Waxed 20/6mm By 242mm By 2000-2350mm	48	March	Internet	14833	£5,616.00	£6,739.20
256	Vivace Waxed	5989	Waxed	Superior Engineered Oak Brushed Waxed 20/6mm By 242mm By 2000-2350mm	45	March	Beautiful Homes	14838	£5,265.00	£6,318.00
257									£5,370.40	

(a) – (b) showing formulas

	A	B	C	D	H	I	J
2							
3							
4	Name	Item number	Finish	Description	Invoice number	Net	Gross
35	Bravura Waxed	7894	Waxed	Prime Engineered Oak Brushed Waxed 15/4mm By 200mm By 1800-2200r	14617	=VLOOKUP(B35,'Price List'!$A$5:$D$18,4, FALSE)*E35	=(I35*$G$1)+I35
39	Bravura Waxed	7894	Waxed	Prime Engineered Oak Brushed Waxed 15/4mm By 200mm By 1800-2200r	14621	=VLOOKUP(B39,'Price List'!$A$5:$D$18,4, FALSE)*E39	=(I39*$G$1)+I39
41	Dolce Natural	6814	Unfinished	Prime Engineered Oak Brushed Unfinished 15/4mm By 300mm By 1800-	14623	=VLOOKUP(B41,'Price List'!$A$5:$D$18,4, FALSE)*E41	=(I41*$G$1)+I41
43	Dolce Natural	6814	Unfinished	Prime Engineered Oak Brushed Unfinished 15/4mm By 300mm By 1800-	14625	=VLOOKUP(B43,'Price List'!$A$5:$D$18,4, FALSE)*E43	=(I43*$G$1)+I43
52	Dolce Waxed	6815	Waxed	Prime Engineered Oak Brushed Waxed 15/4mm By 300mm By 1800-2500r	14634	=VLOOKUP(B52,'Price List'!$A$5:$D$18,4, FALSE)*E52	=(I52*$G$1)+I52
84	Vivace Waxed	5989	Waxed	Superior Engineered Oak Brushed Waxed 20/6mm By 242mm By 2000-25	14666	=VLOOKUP(B84,'Price List'!$A$5:$D$18,4, FALSE)*E84	=(I84*$G$1)+I84
131	Dolce Waxed	6815	Waxed	Prime Engineered Oak Brushed Waxed 15/4mm By 300mm By 1800-2500r	14713	=VLOOKUP(B131,'Price List'!$A$5:$D$18,4, FALSE)*E131	=(I131*$G$1)+I131
169	Vivace Waxed	5989	Waxed	Superior Engineered Oak Brushed Waxed 20/6mm By 242mm By 2000-23	14751	=VLOOKUP(B169,'Price List'!$A$5:$D$18,4, FALSE)*E169	=(I169*$G$1)+I169
251	Vivace Waxed	5989	Waxed	Superior Engineered Oak Brushed Waxed 20/6mm By 242mm By 2000-23	14833	=VLOOKUP(B251,'Price List'!$A$5:$D$18,4, FALSE)*E251	=(I251*$G$1)+I251
256	Vivace Waxed	5989	Waxed	Superior Engineered Oak Brushed Waxed 20/6mm By 242mm By 2000-23	14838	=VLOOKUP(B256,'Price List'!$A$5:$D$18,4, FALSE)*E256	=(I256*$G$1)+I256
257						=SUBTOTAL(1,I35,I39,I41,I43,I52,I84,I131,I169,I251,I256)	
258							
259							
260							

Invoices / Price List / Screen Print / Fast Class Flooring 1

(c)

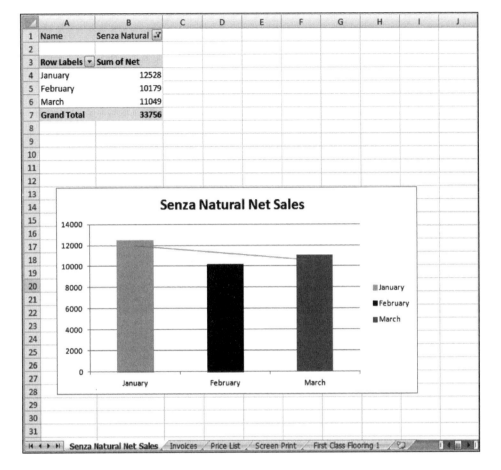

(d)

	A	B	C	D	E	F
1						
2						
3						
4						
5						
6	Partnership appropriation statement for year ended 31 December 20-8					
7		George	Janek	Total		
8	Profit for the year			£159,950		
9	Salary	£20,000		£20,000		
10	Interest on drawings	£600	£720	£1,320		
11	Commission	£3,877	£3,743	£7,620		
12	Residual profit available for appropriation			£133,650		
13	Profit share	£53,460	£80,190	£133,650		
14	Total amount distributed to each partner	£76,737	£83,213	£159,950		
15						
16						
17						
18						
19	Partnership current accounts for year ended 31 December 20-8					
20		George	Janek	George	Janek	
21		Debit	Debit	Credit	Credit	
22	Balance brought down			£7,500	£9,600	
23	Salary			£20,000		
24	Drawings	£56,200	£62,200			
25	Interest on drawings	£600	£720			
26	Commission			£3,877	£3,743	
27	Profit share			£53,460	£80,190	
28	Balance carried down	£28,037	£30,613			
29		£84,837	£93,533	£84,837	£93,533	
30						
31						
32						
33						
34						

Senza Natural Net Sales / Invoices / Price List / Screen Print / **First Class Flooring 1**

(d) showing formulas

	A	B	C	D	E
6	Partnership appropriation statement for year ended 31 December 20-8				
7		George	Janek	Total	
8	Profit for the year			159950	
9	Salary	20000		=C9+B9	
10	Interest on drawings	600	720	=C10+B10	
11	Commission	3877	3743	=C11+B11	
12	Residual profit available for appropriation			=D8-D9-D10-D11	
13	Profit share	=D12/5*2	=D12/5*3	=C13+B13	
14	Total amount distributed to each partner	=B9-B10+B11+B13	=C9-C10+C11+C13	=C14+B14	

	A	B	C	D	E
19	Partnership current accounts for year ended 31 December 20-8				
20		George	Janek	George	Janek
21		Debit	Debit	Credit	Credit
22	Balance brought down			7500	9600
23	Salary			20000	
24	Drawings	56200	62200		
25	Interest on drawings	600	720		
26	Commission			3877	3743
27	Profit share			=+B13	=+C13
28	Balance carried down	=+D29-B24-B25	=+E29-C24-C25		
29		=SUM(B22:B28)	=SUM(C22:C28)	=SUM(D22:D28)	=SUM(E22:E28)

Senza Natural Net Sales / Invoices / Price List / Screen Print / First Class Flooring 1

Answers to practice synoptic assessment 2

Section 1

Task 1.1: 15 marks

(a)

Statement	True	False
You have to do whatever I tell you in my accounts, as I am your client		✔
You have to keep to rules, which tell you how to behave ethically in every situation		✔

(b)

Situation	Comply	Not Comply
Alek produced the financial statements for his sister-in-law's business		✔
Alek accepts a meal for his family for free from a local client who owns a restaurant		✔

(c)   (b) Integrity

(d)

Action	Tick to do
Agree with the client and record the accounts in April	
Inform his manager	✔
Document the request on People First's file	✔
Report People First to the National Crime Agency (NCA)	

(e)

Statement	True	False
By paying the National Minimum Wage, Fruity Fruits is acting ethically		✔
Charging high rents to the pickers raises doubts about Fruity Fruits Limited's ethical approach to business	✔	

(f)   (b)   Make a Suspicious Activity Report to the Money Laundering Reporting Officer

(g)   If Alek informs Patios and Paving he is going to report them for **money laundering** he will be guilty of **tipping off** and will be **liable to be prosecuted**.

Task 1.2: 15 marks

(a)

General ledger code	Dr £	Cr £
Entertaining	210	
VAT control a/c		210

(b)   (b)   Decrease the profit

(c)   (c)   A self-interest threat to objectivity

(d)   (b)   Discuss the situation with Sarah and try to persuade her to report the sale correctly

(e)   (c)   Decline the work and suggest she contact a local specialist in licence applications

(f)   £922 Cr

(g)   (a)   A wages payment made using petty cash which did not have a petty cash slip produced for it

(h)   (a)   A faster payment of £375 has been recorded in the cash book as £275

           (c)   Overdraft charges of £57 have not been entered into the cash book

(i)   (c)   To ensure the cash book accurately reflects the bank transactions of the business

Task 1.3: 15 marks

(a) **Threat 1**

I face a confidentiality issue, as I process the payroll and know Amy is not paying her staff a fair wage, if tips are not included, and is breaking the law by paying below the minimum wage.

Threat 2

I face an intimidation threat to my objectivity, as Amy is suggesting if the minimum wage was paid, I would be responsible for the business ceasing to operate.

(b) As Amy is breaking the law, I am able to break confidentiality and report her to the relevant authorities.

I must record the actions I have taken and conversations I have had to help Amy comply with the legislation.

I could phone the AAT Ethics helpline or, alternatively, seek legal advice prior to reporting this.

(c) (c) It is important to take a long-term view and allow the needs of present generations to be met without compromising the ability of future generations to meet their needs.

(d)

EMAIL

To: Amy Cox

From: Tim Oakley

Date: 12 January 20-5

Subject: Sole Trader or Limited Company

Dear Amy,

Further to our conversation yesterday, I set out below the main issues you should consider while you decide if you wish to trade as a limited company:

(1)   As a sole trader, you own the business and you must produce a set of accounts to support your annual tax return. I produce these for you and they will only be distributed to people or organisations you choose to give them to, such as HMRC.

   If you choose to set up a limited company, you will own shares in the business and you will be the director of it. A limited company must produce a set of accounts at least annually and these will be filed at Companies House, so they will be available to the public.

(2)   The accounts currently are produced using general accounting principles and the format can be tailored to meet your needs.

   A limited company must produce a set of accounts which comply with accounting standards and regulations and the Companies Act 2006. The accounts format is therefore more defined. This is to ensure suppliers, customers, banks and shareholders can easily understand them and compare them with other businesses. There is a much greater administrative burden on you and this will mean additional costs.

(3)   By setting up a limited company you will limit your liability. Currently you are liable for all of the debts of Catering for Occasions. As a shareholder of a limited company you will only be liable up to the value of the investment in the shares you own, as the company is a separate legal entity.

Section 2

Task 2.1: 16 marks

(a) – (c)

	A	B	C	D	E	F	G
1	Catering for Occasions						
2	Year ended 31 December 20-4		Budget	Actual	Variance		
3							
4			£	£	£	% of Budget	
5							
6	Revenue	Food	95,400	104,950	9,550	10.01%	
7	Revenue	Drinks	5,200	6,300	1,100	21.15%	
8	Materials:	Food	33,390	39,500	-6,110	-18.30%	
9	Materials:	Drinks	2,340	2,802	-462	-19.74%	
10	Direct labour:	Cooking staff	15,200	17,200	-2,000	-13.16%	
11	Direct labour:	Waiting staff	15,500	17,050	-1,550	-10.00%	
12	Variable overheads:	Electricity	4,000	4,200	-200	-5.00%	
13	Variable overheads:	Equipment hire	2,000	2,500	-500	-25.00%	
14	Fixed overheads:	Rent and rates	5,000	5,000	0	0.00%	
15	Fixed overheads:	Insurance	1,000	900	100	10.00%	
16	Fixed overheads:	Marketing	1,000	1,500	-500	-50.00%	
17	Operating profit		21,170	20,598	-572		
18					Balanced		
19							

(a) – (c) showing header and footer

Catering for Occasions Year ended 31 December 20-4

Catering for Occasions Year ended 31 December 20-4		Budget	Actual	Variance	
		£	£	£	% of Budget
Revenue	Food	95,400	104,950	9,550	10.01%
Revenue	Drinks	5,200	6,300	1,100	21.15%
Materials:	Food	33,390	39,500	-6,110	-18.30%
Materials:	Drinks	2,340	2,802	-462	-19.74%
Direct labour:	Cooking staff	15,200	17,200	-2,000	-13.16%
Direct labour:	Waiting staff	15,500	17,050	-1,550	-10.00%
Variable overheads:	Electricity	4,000	4,200	-200	-5.00%
Variable overheads:	Equipment hire	2,000	2,500	-500	-25.00%
Fixed overheads:	Rent and rates	5,000	5,000	0	0.00%
Fixed overheads:	Insurance	1,000	900	100	10.00%
Fixed overheads:	Marketing	1,000	1,500	-500	-50.00%
Operating profit		21,170	20,598	-572	
				Balanced	

(a) – (c) 'Variance analysis' to show formulas for reference

	A	B	C	D	E	F
1	Catering for Occasions					
2	Year ended 31 December 20-4					
3						
4			Budget	Actual	Variance	% of Budget
5			£	£	£	
6	Revenue	Food	='Budget and actual data'!C4	='Budget and actual data'!D4	=+D6-C6	=+E6/C6
7	Revenue	Drinks	='Budget and actual data'!C5	='Budget and actual data'!D5	=+D7-C7	=+E7/C7
8	Materials:	Food	='Budget and actual data'!C6	='Budget and actual data'!D6	=+C8-D8	=+E8/C8
9	Materials:	Drinks	='Budget and actual data'!C7	='Budget and actual data'!D7	=+C9-D9	=+E9/C9
10	Direct labour:	Cooking staff	='Budget and actual data'!C8	='Budget and actual data'!D8	=+C10-D10	=+E10/C10
11	Direct labour:	Waiting staff	='Budget and actual data'!C9	='Budget and actual data'!D9	=+C11-D11	=+E11/C11
12	Variable overheads:	Electricity	='Budget and actual data'!C10	='Budget and actual data'!D10	=+C12-D12	=+E12/C12
13	Variable overheads:	Equipment hire	='Budget and actual data'!C11	='Budget and actual data'!D11	=+C13-D13	=+E13/C13
14	Fixed overheads:	Rent and rates	='Budget and actual data'!C12	='Budget and actual data'!D12	=+C14-D14	=+E14/C14
15	Fixed overheads:	Insurance	='Budget and actual data'!C13	='Budget and actual data'!D13	=+C15-D15	=+E15/C15
16	Fixed overheads:	Marketing	='Budget and actual data'!C14	='Budget and actual data'!D14	=+C16-D16	=+E16/C16
17	Operating profit		=SUM(C6:C7)-SUM(C8:C16)	=SUM(D6:D7)-SUM(D8:D16)	=+D17-C17	
18						=IF(SUM(E6:E16)=E17,"Balanced","Check")
19						

(d)

	A	B	C	D	E
1	**Year ended 31 December 20X4**		**Budget**	**Actual**	
2					
3			£	£	
4					
5	Materials:	Food	- 33,390	- 39,500	
6	Revenue	Food	95,400	104,950	
7	Direct labour:	Food	- 15,200	- 17,200	
8	Revenue	Drinks	5,200	6,300	
9	Materials:	Drinks	- 2,340	- 2,802	
10	Food margin		49.07%	45.97%	
11	Drinks margin		55.00%	55.52%	
12					
13					

(e)

	A	B	C	D	E	F	G	H	I
1	Budget sales 20-5								
2	Yearly sales	£130,000							
3									
4	Month	Actual sales	% of total in 20-4	Target 20-5					
5		20-4							
6	1	£4,523	4.3%	£5,603					
7	2	£7,521	7.2%	£9,316					
8	3	£5,154	4.9%	£6,384					
9	4	£6,885	6.6%	£8,528					
10	5	£10,852	10.3%	£13,442					
11	6	£10,548	10.1%	£13,066					
12	7	£12,254	11.7%	£15,179					
13	8	£11,598	11.1%	£14,366					
14	9	£9,956	9.5%	£12,332					
15	10	£8,542	8.1%	£10,581					
16	11	£6,589	6.3%	£8,162					
17	12	£10,528	10.0%	£13,041					
18		£104,950	100%	£130,000					
19									
20									
21									
22									
23									
24									
25									
26									
27									
28									
29									
30									
31									
32									

Budget and actual data / Variance analysis / Food and drink analysis / **Forecast 20-5** / Screen Print

(e) showing formulas

	A	B	C	D
1	Budget sales 20-5			
2	Yearly sales	130000		
3				
4	Month	Actual sales	% of total in 20-4	Target 20-5
5		20-4		
6	1	4523	=+B6/$B$18	=+C6*$B$2
7	2	7521	=+B7/$B$18	=+C7*$B$2
8	3	5154	=+B8/$B$18	=+C8*$B$2
9	4	6885	=+B9/$B$18	=+C9*$B$2
10	5	10852	=+B10/$B$18	=+C10*$B$2
11	6	10548	=+B11/$B$18	=+C11*$B$2
12	7	12254	=+B12/$B$18	=+C12*$B$2
13	8	11598	=+B13/$B$18	=+C13*$B$2
14	9	9956	=+B14/$B$18	=+C14*$B$2
15	10	8542	=+B15/$B$18	=+C15*$B$2
16	11	6589	=+B16/$B$18	=+C16*$B$2
17	12	10528	=+B17/$B$18	=+C17*$B$2
18		=SUM(B6:B17)	=SUM(C6:C17)	=SUM(D6:D17)
19				
20				
21				
22				
23				
24				
25				
26				
27				
28				
29				
30				
31				
32				

Budget and actual data / Variance analysis / Food and drink analysis / Forecast 20-5 / Screen Print

Task 2.2: 30 marks

(a) – (b) (subtotal)

1 2 3		A	B	C	D	E	F	G	H
	1	Date	Job	Person	Hours	Wages rate	Gross Wages		3
	2	1/1/20X6	Smith wedding	Aisha Patel	5	£7.20	£36.00		
	3	1/1/20X6	Smith wedding	Charlotte Pale	4	£7.20	£28.80		
	4	1/1/20X6	Smith wedding	David Howel	5	£7.20	£36.00		
	5	1/1/20X6	Smith wedding	Eddie Marsh	4	£7.20	£28.80		
	6	1/1/20X6	Smith wedding	Edyta Grokotov	7	£7.20	£50.40		
	7	1/1/20X6	Smith wedding	Fiona Dee	3	£7.20	£21.60		
	8	1/1/20X6	Smith wedding	Penny Davis	8	£10.00	£80.00		
	9	1/1/20X6	Smith wedding	Sally Smith	8	£8.50	£68.00		
	10		Smith wedding Total				£349.60		
	11	15/1/20X6	Jamal Party	Aisha Patel	7	£7.20	£50.40		
	12	15/1/20X6	Jamal Party	Charlotte Pale	6	£7.20	£43.20		
	13	15/1/20X6	Jamal Party	David Howel	6	£7.20	£43.20		
	14	15/1/20X6	Jamal Party	Eddie Marsh	9	£7.20	£64.80		
	15	15/1/20X6	Jamal Party	Edyta Grokotov	4	£7.20	£28.80		
	16	15/1/20X6	Jamal Party	Fiona Dee	4	£7.20	£28.80		
	17	15/1/20X6	Jamal Party	Penny Davis	8	£10.00	£80.00		
	18	15/1/20X6	Jamal Party	Sally Smith	5	£8.50	£42.50		
	19		Jamal Party Total				£381.70		
	20	16/1/20X6	Grosvenor wedding	Aisha Patel	6	£7.20	£43.20		
	21	16/1/20X6	Grosvenor wedding	Charlotte Pale	5	£7.20	£36.00		
	22	16/1/20X6	Grosvenor wedding	David Howel	4	£7.20	£28.80		
	23	16/1/20X6	Grosvenor wedding	Eddie Marsh	4	£7.20	£28.80		
	24	16/1/20X6	Grosvenor wedding	Edyta Grokotov	5	£7.20	£36.00		
	25	16/1/20X6	Grosvenor wedding	Fiona Dee	3	£7.20	£21.60		
	26	16/1/20X6	Grosvenor wedding	Penny Davis	9	£10.00	£90.00		
	27	16/1/20X6	Grosvenor wedding	Sally Smith	4	£8.50	£34.00		
	28		Grosvenor wedding Total				£318.40		
	29	22/1/20X6	Zuckerman birthday	Aisha Patel	6	£7.20	£43.20		
	30	22/1/20X6	Zuckerman birthday	Charlotte Pale	4	£7.20	£28.80		
	31	22/1/20X6	Zuckerman birthday	David Howel	4	£7.20	£28.80		
	32	22/1/20X6	Zuckerman birthday	Eddie Marsh	7	£7.20	£50.40		
	33	22/1/20X6	Zuckerman birthday	Fiona Dee	4	£7.20	£28.80		
	34	22/1/20X6	Zuckerman birthday	Odette Partridge	9	£7.20	£64.80		
	35	22/1/20X6	Zuckerman birthday	Penny Davis	9	£10.00	£90.00		
	36	22/1/20X6	Zuckerman birthday	Sally Smith	4	£8.50	£34.00		
	37		Zuckerman birthday Total				£368.80		
	38	29/1/20X6	Moore 50th wedding anniversary	Aisha Patel	7	£7.20	£50.40		
	39	29/1/20X6	Moore 50th wedding anniversary	Charlotte Pale	4	£7.20	£28.80		
	40	29/1/20X6	Moore 50th wedding anniversary	David Howel	3	£7.20	£21.60		
	41	29/1/20X6	Moore 50th wedding anniversary	Eddie Marsh	4	£7.20	£28.80		
	42	29/1/20X6	Moore 50th wedding anniversary	Fiona Dee	6	£7.20	£43.20		
	43	29/1/20X6	Moore 50th wedding anniversary	Odette Partridge	8	£7.20	£57.60		
	44	29/1/20X6	Moore 50th wedding anniversary	Penny Davis	8	£10.00	£80.00		
	45	29/1/20X6	Moore 50th wedding anniversary	Sally Smith	6	£8.50	£51.00		
	46		Moore 50th wedding anniversary Total				£361.40		
	47	30/1/20X6	Wilber birthday	Charlotte Pale	6	£7.20	£43.20		
	48	30/1/20X6	Wilber birthday	David Howel	4	£7.20	£28.80		
	49	30/1/20X6	Wilber birthday	Fiona Dee	5	£7.20	£36.00		
	50	30/1/20X6	Wilber birthday	Penny Davis	7	£10.00	£70.00		
	51	30/1/20X6	Wilber birthday	Sally Smith	4	£8.50	£34.00		
	52		Wilber birthday Total				£212.00		
	53	31/1/20X6	Hanson Birthday party	Aisha Patel	9	£7.20	£64.80		
	54	31/1/20X6	Hanson Birthday party	Charlotte Pale	4	£7.20	£28.80		
	55	31/1/20X6	Hanson Birthday party	David Howel	6	£7.20	£43.20		
	56	31/1/20X6	Hanson Birthday party	Eddie Marsh	4	£7.20	£28.80		
	57	31/1/20X6	Hanson Birthday party	Edyta Grokotov	4	£7.20	£28.80		
	58	31/1/20X6	Hanson Birthday party	Fiona Dee	7	£7.20	£50.40		
	59	31/1/20X6	Hanson Birthday party	Penny Davis	7	£10.00	£70.00		
	60	31/1/20X6	Hanson Birthday party	Sally Smith	3	£8.50	£25.50		
	61		Hanson Birthday party Total				£340.30		
	62		Grand Total				£2,332.20		
	63								

(a) – (b) excerpt of 'January working' to show formulas for reference

	Date	Job	Person	Hours	Wages rate	Gross Wages		3
38	29/1/20X6	Moore 50th wedding anniversary	Aisha Patel	7	=VLOOKUP(C38,Wage rate!$A$2:$B$10,2)	=D38*E38		
39	29/1/20X6	Moore 50th wedding anniversary	Charlotte Pate	4	=VLOOKUP(C39,Wage rate!$A$2:$B$10,2)	=D39*E39		
40	29/1/20X6	Moore 50th wedding anniversary	David Howell	3	=VLOOKUP(C40,Wage rate!$A$2:$B$10,2)	=D40*E40		
41	29/1/20X6	Moore 50th wedding anniversary	Eddie Marsh	4	=VLOOKUP(C41,Wage rate!$A$2:$B$10,2)	=D41*E41		
42	29/1/20X6	Moore 50th wedding anniversary	Fiona Dee	6	=VLOOKUP(C42,Wage rate!$A$2:$B$10,2)	=D42*E42		
43	29/1/20X6	Moore 50th wedding anniversary	Odette Partridge	8	=VLOOKUP(C43,Wage rate!$A$2:$B$10,2)	=D43*E43		
44	29/1/20X6	Moore 50th wedding anniversary	Penny Davis	8	=VLOOKUP(C44,Wage rate!$A$2:$B$10,2)	=D44*E44		
45	29/1/20X6	Moore 50th wedding anniversary	Sally Smith	6	=VLOOKUP(C45,Wage rate!$A$2:$B$10,2)	=D45*E45		
46		Moore 50th wedding anniversary Total				=SUBTOTAL(9,F38:F45)		
47	30/1/20X6	Wilber birthday	Charlotte Pate	6	=VLOOKUP(C47,Wage rate!$A$2:$B$10,2)	=D47*E47		
48	30/1/20X6	Wilber birthday	David Howell	4	=VLOOKUP(C48,Wage rate!$A$2:$B$10,2)	=D48*E48		
49	30/1/20X6	Wilber birthday	Fiona Dee	5	=VLOOKUP(C49,Wage rate!$A$2:$B$10,2)	=D49*E49		
50	30/1/20X6	Wilber birthday	Penny Davis	7	=VLOOKUP(C50,Wage rate!$A$2:$B$10,2)	=D50*E50		
51	30/1/20X6	Wilber birthday	Sally Smith	4	=VLOOKUP(C51,Wage rate!$A$2:$B$10,2)	=D51*E51		
52		Wilber birthday Total				=SUBTOTAL(9,F47:F51)		
53	31/1/20X6	Hanson Birthday party	Aisha Patel	9	=VLOOKUP(C53,Wage rate!$A$2:$B$10,2)	=D53*E53		
54	31/1/20X6	Hanson Birthday party	Charlotte Pate	4	=VLOOKUP(C54,Wage rate!$A$2:$B$10,2)	=D54*E54		
55	31/1/20X6	Hanson Birthday party	David Howell	6	=VLOOKUP(C55,Wage rate!$A$2:$B$10,2)	=D55*E55		
56	31/1/20X6	Hanson Birthday party	Eddie Marsh	4	=VLOOKUP(C56,Wage rate!$A$2:$B$10,2)	=D56*E56		
57	31/1/20X6	Hanson Birthday party	Edyta Grokcrov	4	=VLOOKUP(C57,Wage rate!$A$2:$B$10,2)	=D57*E57		
58	31/1/20X6	Hanson Birthday party	Fiona Dee	7	=VLOOKUP(C58,Wage rate!$A$2:$B$10,2)	=D58*E58		
59	31/1/20X6	Hanson Birthday party	Penny Davis	7	=VLOOKUP(C59,Wage rate!$A$2:$B$10,2)	=D59*E59		
60	31/1/20X6	Hanson Birthday party	Sally Smith	3	=VLOOKUP(C60,Wage rate!$A$2:$B$10,2)	=D60*E60		
61		Hanson Birthday party Total				=SUBTOTAL(9,F53:F60)		
62		Grand Total				=SUBTOTAL(9,F2:F60)		

(b)

	A	B	F	G	H	I	J	K	L	M	N	O	P	C
1	Date	Job	Gross Wages		3									
10		Smith wedding Total	£349.60											
19		Jamal Party Total	£381.70											
28		Grosvenor wedding Total	£318.40											
37		Zuckerman birthday Total	£368.80											
46		Moore 50th wedding anniversary Total	£361.40											
52		Wilber birthday Total	£212.00											
61		Hanson Birthday party Total	£340.30											
62		Grand Total	£2,332.20											

Analysis of January wages by job

(c)

	A	B	C	D	E	F	G	H
1	January jobs							
2					Sales	Food/ drink	Wages	Gross margin
3							costs	
4					£	£	£	£
5	Smith wedding				1,500.00	450.05	349.60	700.35
6	Jamal Party				1,450.00	450.00	381.70	618.30
7	Grosvenor wedding				1,200.00	360.00	318.40	521.60
8	Zuckerman party				1,650.00	545.00	368.80	736.20
9	Moore 50th wedding anniversary				1,500.00	515.00	361.40	623.60
10	Wilber birthday				1,150.00	350.00	212.00	588.00
11	Hanson birthday party				1,200.00	400.00	340.30	459.70
12					9,650.00	3,070.05	2,332.20	4,247.75
13								
14								

(c) showing formulas

	A	B	C	D	E	F	G	H
1	January jobs							
2					Sales	Food/ drink	Wages	Gross margin
3							costs	
4					£	£	£	£
5	Smith wedding				1500	450.05	=+'Analysis wages by job'!F10	=E5-SUM(F5:G5)
6	Jamal Party				1450	450	=+'Analysis wages by job'!F19	=E6-SUM(F6:G6)
7	Grosvenor wedding				1200	360	=+'Analysis wages by job'!F28	=E7-SUM(F7:G7)
8	Zuckerman party				1650	545	=+'Analysis wages by job'!F37	=E8-SUM(F8:G8)
9	Moore 50th wedding anniversary				1500	515	=+'Analysis wages by job'!F46	=E9-SUM(F9:G9)
10	Wilber birthday				1150	350	=+'Analysis wages by job'!F52	=E10-SUM(F10:G10)
11	Hanson birthday party				1200	400	=+'Analysis wages by job'!F61	=E11-SUM(F11:G11)
12					=SUM(E5:E11)	=SUM(F5:F11)	=SUM(G5:G11)	=SUM(H5:H11)
13								

(d) – (e)

	B	C	D	E	F	G	H	I	J	K	L	M
1 **Catering for Occasions**												
2 EXTENDED TRIAL BALANCE AS AT 31 DECEMBER 20X5				Ledger Balances		Adjustments		Statement of profit or loss		Statement of financial position		
3				DR	CR	DR	CR	DR	CR	DR	CR	
4 Opening inventory				3540				3540				
5 Purchases				41859				41859				
6 Prepayment						400				400		
7 Bank				25697						25697		
8 Cash				464						464		
9 Sales ledger control account				4313						4313		
10 Van at cost				20000						20000		
11 Equipment at cost				6595						6595		
12 Depreciation van					14400		3600				18000	
13 Depreciation equipment					4150						4150	
14 Value Added Tax					1363						1363	
15 Purchase ledger control					7880						7880	
16 Accruals							452				452	
17 Capital					25000						25000	
18 Drawings				14400						14400		
19 Sales revenue					111250				111250			
20 Rent paid				4500				4500				
21 Interest paid				180				180				
22 Telephone				250				250				
23 Light Heat				3789		452		4241				
24 Wages				34189				34189				
25 Insurance				1500			400	1100				
26 Travel expenses				650				650				
27 Marketing				1500				1500				
28 Other expenses				467				467				
29 Depreciation				150		3600		3750				
30												
31 Closing inventory - Statement of profit or loss									3097			
32 Closing inventory - Statement of financial position										3097		
33 Profit / loss for the year								18121			18121	
34				164043	164043	4452	4452	114347	114347	74966	74966	
35					OK		OK		OK		OK	
36 Adjustments												
37 Insurance prepayment 6/12 x £800 = £400												
38 Depreciation £3600												
39 Accrual electricity £452												
40												

(d) – (e) showing formulas

	A	B	C	D	I	J	K	L	M
1	Catering for Occasions								
2	EXTENDED TRIAL BALANCE AS AT 31 DECEMBER 20X5				Statement of profit or loss		Statement of financial position		
3					DR	CR	DR	CR	
4	Opening inventory				=+E4+G4-H4				
5	Purchases				=+E5+G5-H5				
6	Prepayment						=+E6+G6-H6		
7	Bank						=+E7+G7-H7		
8	Cash						=+E8+G8-H8		
9	Sales ledger control account						=+E9+G9-H9		
10	Van at cost						=+E10+G10-H10		
11	Equipment at cost						=+E11+G11-H11		
12	Depreciation van							=+F12+H12-G12	
13	Depreciation equipment							=+F13+H13-G13	
14	Value Added Tax							=+F14+H14-G14	
15	Purchase ledger control							=+F15+H15-G15	
16	Accruals							=+F16+H16-G16	
17	Capital							=+F17+H17-G17	
18	Drawings						=+E18+G18-H18		
19	Sales revenue					=+F19+H19-G19			
20	Rent paid				=+E20+G20-H20				
21	Interest paid				=+E21+G21-H21				
22	Telephone				=+E22+G22-H22				
23	Light Heat				=+E23+G23-H23				
24	Wages				=+E24+G24-H24				
25	Insurance				=+E25+G25-H25				
26	Travel expenses				=+E26+G26-H26				
27	Marketing				=+E27+G27-H27				
28	Other expenses				=+E28+G28-H28				
29	Depreciation				=+E29+G29-H29				
30									
31	Closing inventory - Statement of profit or loss					3097			
32	Closing inventory - Statement of financial positio						3097		
33	Profit / loss for the year				18121			18121	
34					=SUM(I4:I33)	=SUM(J4:J33)	=SUM(K4:K33)	=SUM(L4:L33)	
35						=+IF(I34-J34=0,"OK"		=+IF(K34-L34=0,"OK	
36	Adjustments								
37	Insurance prepayment 6/12 x £800 = £400								
38	Depreciation £3600								
39	Accrual electricity £452								

(f) Current assets formula

	A	B	C	D	E	F	G	H	I	J	K	L	M	N	O
1	A	B	C	D	E	F	G	H	I	J		K			
2 / 35							Catering for Occasions								
3 / 36															
4 / 37						STATEMENT OF FINANCIAL POSITION									
5 / 38															
6 / 39										£				£	
7 / 40			Non-current Assets												
8 / 41				Van										2,000	
9 / 42				Equipment										2,445	
10 / 43														4,445	
11 / 44															
12 / 45			Current Assets												
13 / 46				Inventory						3,097					
14 / 47				Trade receivables						4,313					
15 / 48				Prepaid insurance						400					
16 / 49				Bank						25,697					
17 / 50				Cash						464					
18 / 51														30,874	
19 / 52															
20 / 53			Current liabilities												
21 / 54				Trade payables						7,880					
22 / 55				Accrued electricity						452					
23 / 56				Value Added Tax						1,363					
24 / 57														9,695	
25 / 58			Net current Assets												21,179
26 / 59															
27 / 60			NET ASSETS												25,624
28 / 61															
29 / 62															
30 / 63			FINANCED BY:												
31 / 64				Capital											
32 / 65				Opening capital										25,000	
33 / 66				Add Profit for the year										18,121	
34 / 67														43,121	
35 / 68				Less Drawings										14,400	

January working | Wage rate | Job analysis | Analysis wages by job | Screen print | Extended trial balance | Financial statements | Current ass

(f)

	Catering for Occasions	£	£
	STATEMENT OF PROFIT OR LOSS		
Sales Revenue			111,250
Opening inventory		3,540	
Purchases		41,859	
		45,399	
Closing inventory		3,097	
Cost of Sales			42,302
Gross Profit			68,948
Less Expenses			
Rent		4,500	
Interest		180	
Telephone		250	
Light Heat		4,241	
Wages		34,189	
Insurance		1,100	
Travel expenses		650	
Marketing		1,500	
Other expenses		467	
Depreciation		3,750	
			50,827
Profit for the year			18,121
		Balanced	

	Catering for Occasions	£	£
	STATEMENT OF FINANCIAL POSITION		
Non-current Assets			
Van			2,000
Equipment			2,445
			4,445
Current Assets			
Inventory		3,097	
Trade receivables		4,313	
Prepaid insurance		400	
Bank		25,697	
Cash		464	
			33,971
Current liabilities			
Trade payables		7,880	
Accrued electricity		452	
Value Added Tax		1,363	
			9,695
Net current Assets			24,276
NET ASSETS			28,721
FINANCED BY:			
Capital			
Opening capital			25,000
Add Profit for the year			18,121
			43,121
Less Drawings			14,400
			28,721

Answers to practice synoptic assessment 3

Section 1

Task 1.1: 15 marks

(a)

Statement	True	False
How I behave in my personal life is not important to the AAT, as I only need to comply with the Code of Ethics at work		✔
If I have an ethical problem, I need to use a methodical approach to resolve it	✔	

(b)

Situation	Comply	Not Comply
Daisy completes the VAT return for a client who sells and buys overseas, when she has no experience of imports and exports		✔
Daisy attends a training course on new International Accounting Standards	✔	

(c)   (a) Objectivity

(d)   (c) A self-review threat

Action	Tick to do
Inform the client	✔
Complete the work, then inform her manager once the accounts are finished	
Inform her manager and request he reviews the work in detail once she has performed it	✔
Request to be removed from the work for this year end	✔

(e)

Action	
(a) Immediately inform Martin, Plum and Holsworth's Money Laundering Officer of her concerns	✔
(b) Complete a Suspicious Activity Report (SAR) and send it to the National Crime Agency (NCA)	

(f)

Action	
Correct the error on this year's return and do not tell anyone	
Advise HMRC of the error without disclosing it to Excellence in Recruitment or Martin, Plum and Holsworth	
Tell Martin, Plum and Holsworth of the error and recommend the error be disclosed to Excellence in Recruitment	✔

(g) If Daisy does not tell the MRLO of their money laundering she will be guilty of **failure to disclose** and could be imprisoned for up to **five** years.

Task 1.2: 15 marks

(a)

General ledger code	Dr £	Cr £
Vehicles		6,000
VAT control a/c	6,000	

(b) (b) Decrease the depreciation charge

(c) (b) A self-interest threat to objectivity

(d) (a) Tell Jason and Claire about your concerns

(e) (a) Request that the visit from the bank be postponed

(f) 20-2: £17,500.00 x 25% = £4,375.00, carrying value = £17,500.00 – £4,375.00 = £13,125.00

20-3: £13,125.00 x 25% = £3,281.25, carrying value = £13,125.00 – £3,281.25 = £9,843.75

20-4: £9,843.75 x 25% = £2,460.94, carrying value = £9,843.75 – £7,382.81

Depreciation = £4,375.00 + £3,281.25 + £2,460.94 = £10,117.19

(g) £5,000.00 – £7,382.81 = £2,382.81 loss

(h) (c) To apply the accruals concept, matching cost to revenue

(i) (d) Hire purchase

Task 1.3: 15 marks

(a) **Threat 1**

I am facing a breach of integrity as I will be dishonestly moving expenses form one year into the next. I will not be behaving professionally, as the information will be used for obtaining a mortgage incorrectly. If this action should be discovered I would bring the accounting profession into disrepute.

Threat 2

I am also facing a self-interest threat as she has offered me the complete product range if I do it, which is worth a lot of money.

(b) Firstly I must explain to Claire that I am unable to do this. If she insists that I must, then I will inform Jason of her request.

If both Jason and Claire are unhappy and demand I change the accounts, I will have to resign.

(c)

EMAIL

To: Claire Giles; Jason Taylor

From: Serena Parry

Date: 6 April 20-5

Subject: Charity information

Dear Claire and Jason,

I set out below the information regarding charities you requested:

(1) A charity is an organisation run by trustees, which uses its resources to fund charitable activities under its control.

(2) The trustees manage the charity, where funds will come in and then be distributed for the benefit of the public. The charity will have a trust deed, which sets out the charity's name, object and powers, how to appoint and remove trustees and whom the charity can make distributions to.

(3) If the charity is unincorporated, the trustees will be liable for the debts of the charity. If it is limited, liability will be limited. Charities do not pay tax. If it is a charitable company (with limited liability) it must be registered with Companies House.

(4) The Charities Act is the main regulation that governs charities. Charities must produce accounts under the Statement of Recommended Practice (SORP).

All charities are registered with the Charity Commission, who monitor what they do. Charities submit financial statements to the Charity Commission each year, which are publically available.

Please contact me if you require anything further.

Best wishes

Serena

Section 2

Task 2.1: 25 marks

(a) – (c)

	A	B	C	D	F	G	H	I	J	K
1	Beautiful tableware									
2	Budgeted overhead rates 20X6									
3										
4	Apportionment basis									
5	Overhead	Basis of apportionment			Moulding	Glazing	Finishing	Stores	Maintenance	Total
6	Buildings insurance	Floor space (sq metres)			500	150	100	50	25	825
7	Depreciation of machinery	Value of machinery			35000	15000	5000	2000	3000	60000
8	Lighting and heating	Floor space (sq metres)			500	150	100	50	25	825
9	Rent and rates	Floor space (sq metres)			500	150	100	50	25	825
10	Supervisors' salaries	Number of employees			5	2	1	0.5	0.5	9
11										
12										
13	Apportionment £									
14	Overhead	Basis of apportionment			Moulding	Glazing	Finishing	Stores	Maintenance	Total
15	Buildings insurance	Floor space (sq metres)			£2,000.00	£600.00	£400.00	£200.00	£100.00	£3,300.00 OK
16	Depreciation of machinery	Value of machinery			£8,750.00	£3,750.00	£1,250.00	£500.00	£750.00	£15,000.00 OK
17	Lighting and heating	Floor space (sq metres)			£6,000.00	£1,800.00	£1,200.00	£600.00	£300.00	£9,900.00 OK
18	Rent and rates	Floor space (sq metres)			£11,000.00	£3,300.00	£2,200.00	£1,100.00	£550.00	£18,150.00 OK
19	Supervisors' salaries	Number of employees			£20,000.00	£8,000.00	£4,000.00	£2,000.00	£2,000.00	£36,000.00 OK
20										£0.00
21					£47,750.00	£17,450.00	£9,050.00	£4,400.00	£3,700.00	£82,350.00
22	Stores				£2,640.00	£1,320.00	£440.00	-£4,400.00		£0.00
23	Maintenance				£2,775.00	£555.00	£370.00		-£3,700.00	£0.00
24										£0.00
25	Total				£53,165.00	£19,325.00	£9,860.00	£0.00	£0.00	£82,350.00
26										
27	OAR				£2.12	£5.00	£8.00			
28										
29										
30										

Apportionment calculation / Basis of apportionment / Revised apportionment / Screen print

Formulas columns A-G

	A	B	C	D	F	G
1	Beautiful tableware					
2	Budgeted overhead rates 20X6					
3						
4	Apportionment basis					
5	Overhead	Basis of apportionment			Moulding	Glazing
6	Buildings insurance	Floor space (sq metres)			=VLOOKUP($B6,'Basis of apportionment'!$A$4:$G$6,2)	=VLOOKUP($B6,'Basis of apportionment'!$A$4:$G$6,3)
7	Depreciation of machinery	Value of machinery			=VLOOKUP($B7,'Basis of apportionment'!$A$4:$G$6,2)	=VLOOKUP($B7,'Basis of apportionment'!$A$4:$G$6,3)
8	Lighting and heating	Floor space (sq metres)			=VLOOKUP($B8,'Basis of apportionment'!$A$4:$G$6,2)	=VLOOKUP($B8,'Basis of apportionment'!$A$4:$G$6,3)
9	Rent and rates	Floor space (sq metres)			=VLOOKUP($B9,'Basis of apportionment'!$A$4:$G$6,2)	=VLOOKUP($B9,'Basis of apportionment'!$A$4:$G$6,3)
10	Supervisors' salaries	Number of employees			=VLOOKUP($B10,'Basis of apportionment'!$A$4:$G$6,2)	=VLOOKUP($B10,'Basis of apportionment'!$A$4:$G$6,3)
11						
12						
13	Apportionment £					
14	Overhead	Basis of apportionment			Moulding	Glazing
15	Buildings insurance	Floor space (sq metres)			=+$E15*F6/$K6	=+$E15*G6/$K6
16	Depreciation of machinery	Value of machinery			=+$E16*F7/$K7	=+$E16*G7/$K7
17	Lighting and heating	Floor space (sq metres)			=+$E17*F8/$K8	=+$E17*G8/$K8
18	Rent and rates	Floor space (sq metres)			=+$E18*F9/$K9	=+$E18*G9/$K9
19	Supervisors' salaries	Number of employees			=+$E19*F10/$K10	=+$E19*G10/$K10
20						
21					=SUM(F15:F20)	=SUM(G15:G20)
22	Stores				=+H21*0.6	=+H21*0.3
23	Maintenance				=0.75*J21	=0.15*J21
24						
25	Total				=SUM(F21:F24)	=SUM(G21:G24)
26						
27	OAR				=+F25/25100	=+G25/3865
28						
29						
30						

Apportionment calculation | Basis of apportionment | Revised apportionment | Screen print

Formulas columns H – I

	A	B	C	D	H	I
1	Beautiful tableware					
2	Budgeted overhead rates 20X6					
3						
4	Apportionment basis					
5	Overhead	Basis of apportionment			Finishing	Stores
6	Buildings insurance	Floor space (sq metres)			=VLOOKUP($B6,'Basis of apportionment'!$A$4:$G$6,4)	=VLOOKUP($B6,'Basis of apportionment'!$A$4:$G$6,5)
7	Depreciation of machinery	Value of machinery			=VLOOKUP($B7,'Basis of apportionment'!$A$4:$G$6,4)	=VLOOKUP($B7,'Basis of apportionment'!$A$4:$G$6,5)
8	Lighting and heating	Floor space (sq metres)			=VLOOKUP($B8,'Basis of apportionment'!$A$4:$G$6,4)	=VLOOKUP($B8,'Basis of apportionment'!$A$4:$G$6,5)
9	Rent and rates	Floor space (sq metres)			=VLOOKUP($B9,'Basis of apportionment'!$A$4:$G$6,4)	=VLOOKUP($B9,'Basis of apportionment'!$A$4:$G$6,5)
10	Supervisors' salaries	Number of employees			=VLOOKUP($B10,'Basis of apportionment'!$A$4:$G$6,4)	=VLOOKUP($B10,'Basis of apportionment'!$A$4:$G$6,5)
11						
12						
13	Apportionment £					
14	Overhead	Basis of apportionment			Finishing	Stores
15	Buildings insurance	Floor space (sq metres)			=+$E15*H6/$K6	=+$E15*I6/$K6
16	Depreciation of machinery	Value of machinery			=+$E16*H7/$K7	=+$E16*I7/$K7
17	Lighting and heating	Floor space (sq metres)			=+$E17*H8/$K8	=+$E17*I8/$K8
18	Rent and rates	Floor space (sq metres)			=+$E18*H9/$K9	=+$E18*I9/$K9
19	Supervisors' salaries	Number of employees			=+$E19*H10/$K10	=+$E19*I10/$K10
20						
21					=SUM(H15:H20)	=SUM(I15:I20)
22	Stores				=H21*0.1	-4400
23	Maintenance				0.1*'21	
24						
25	Total				=SUM(H21:H24)	=SUM(I21:I24)
26						
27	OAR				=H25/1232	
28						
29						
30						

Apportionment calculation / Basis of apportionment / Revised apportionment / Screen print

Formulas columns J- L

	A	B	C	D	J	K	L
1	**Beautiful tableware**						
2	**Budgeted overhead rates 20X6**						
3							
4	**Apportionment basis**						
5	Overhead	Basis of apportionment			Maintenance	Total	
6	Buildings insurance	Floor space (sq metres)			=VLOOKUP($B6,'Basis of apportionment'!$A$4:$G$6,6)	=VLOOKUP($B6,'Basis of apportionment'!$A$4:$G$6,7)	
7	Depreciation of machinery	Value of machinery			=VLOOKUP($B7,'Basis of apportionment'!$A$4:$G$6,6)	=VLOOKUP($B7,'Basis of apportionment'!$A$4:$G$6,7)	
8	Lighting and heating	Floor space (sq metres)			=VLOOKUP($B8,'Basis of apportionment'!$A$4:$G$6,6)	=VLOOKUP($B8,'Basis of apportionment'!$A$4:$G$6,7)	
9	Rent and rates	Floor space (sq metres)			=VLOOKUP($B9,'Basis of apportionment'!$A$4:$G$6,6)	=VLOOKUP($B9,'Basis of apportionment'!$A$4:$G$6,7)	
10	Supervisors' salaries	Number of employees			=VLOOKUP($B10,'Basis of apportionment'!$A$4:$G$6,6)	=VLOOKUP($B10,'Basis of apportionment'!$A$4:$G$6,7)	
11							
12							
13	**Apportionment £**						
14	Overhead	Basis of apportionment			Maintenance	Total	
15	Buildings insurance	Floor space (sq metres)			=$E15*J6/$K6	=SUM(F15:J15)	=IF(K15=E15,"OK","Error")
16	Depreciation of machinery	Value of machinery			=$E16*J7/$K7	=SUM(F16:J16)	=IF(K16=E16,"OK","Error")
17	Lighting and heating	Floor space (sq metres)			=$E17*J8/$K8	=SUM(F17:J17)	=IF(K17=E17,"OK","Error")
18	Rent and rates	Floor space (sq metres)			=$E18*J9/$K9	=SUM(F18:J18)	=IF(K18=E18,"OK","Error")
19	Supervisors' salaries	Number of employees			=$E19*J10/$K10	=SUM(F19:J19)	=IF(K19=E19,"OK","Error")
20						=SUM(F20:J20)	
21					=SUM(J15:J20)	=SUM(F21:J21)	
22	Stores					=SUM(F22:J22)	
23	Maintenance				-3700	=SUM(F23:J23)	
24						=SUM(F24:J24)	
25	Total				=SUM(J21:J24)	=SUM(K21:K24)	
26							
27	OAR						
28							
29							
30							

Apportionment calculation | Basis of apportionment | Revised apportionment | Screen print

(d) Screen print of formulas

	A	B	C	D	E	F	G
1	**Beautiful tableware**						
2	**Budgeted overhead rates 20X6**						
3							
4	Apportionment basis						
5	Overhead	Basis of apportionment				Moulding	Glazing
6	Buildings insurance	Floor space (sq metres)				=VLOOKUP($B6,'Basis of apportionment'!$A$4:$G$6,2)	=VLOOKUP($B6,'Basis of apportionment'!$A$4:$G$6,3)
7	Depreciation of machinery	Value of machinery				=VLOOKUP($B7,'Basis of apportionment'!$A$4:$G$6,2)	=VLOOKUP($B7,'Basis of apportionment'!$A$4:$G$6,3)
8	Lighting and heating	Floor space (sq metres)				=VLOOKUP($B8,'Basis of apportionment'!$A$4:$G$6,2)	=VLOOKUP($B8,'Basis of apportionment'!$A$4:$G$6,3)
9	Rent and rates	Floor space (sq metres)				=VLOOKUP($B9,'Basis of apportionment'!$A$4:$G$6,2)	=VLOOKUP($B9,'Basis of apportionment'!$A$4:$G$6,3)
10	Supervisors' salaries	Number of employees				=VLOOKUP($B10,'Basis of apportionment'!$A$4:$G$6,2)	=VLOOKUP($B10,'Basis of apportionment'!$A$4:$G$6,3)
11							
12							
13	Apportionment £						
14	Overhead	Basis of apportionment			Total	Moulding	Glazing
15	Buildings insurance	Floor space (sq metres)			3300	=$E15*F6/$K6	=$E15*G6/$K6
16	Depreciation of machinery	Value of machinery			15000	=$E16*F7/$K7	=$E16*G7/$K7
17	Lighting and heating	Floor space (sq metres)			9900	=$E17*F8/$K8	=$E17*G8/$K8
18	Rent and rates	Floor space (sq metres)			=18150*1.1	=$E18*F9/$K9	=$E18*G9/$K9
19	Supervisors' salaries	Number of employees			=36000*1.1	=$E19*F10/$K10	=$E19*G10/$K10
20							
21					=SUM(E15:E20)	=SUM(F15:F20)	=SUM(G15:G20)
22	Stores					=I21*0.6	=I21*0.3
23	Maintenance					=0.75*J21	=0.15*J21
24							
25	Total				=SUM(E21:E24)	=SUM(F21:F24)	=SUM(G21:G24)
26							
27	OAR					=F25/25100	=G25/3865
28							
29							

Apportionment calculation | Basis of apportionment | Revised apportionment | Screen print

(d) Revised apportionment

Beautiful tableware
Budgeted overhead rates 20X6

Apportionment basis

	Overhead	Basis of apportionment	Moulding	Glazing	Finishing	Stores	Maintenance	Total
6	Buildings insurance	Floor space (sq metres)	500	150	100	50	25	825
7	Depreciation of machinery	Value of machinery	35000	15000	5000	2000	3000	60000
8	Lighting and heating	Floor space (sq metres)	500	150	100	50	25	825
9	Rent and rates	Floor space (sq metres)	500	150	100	50	25	825
10	Supervisors' salaries	Number of employees	5	2	1	0.5	0.5	9

Apportionment £

	Overhead	Basis of apportionment	Total	Moulding	Glazing	Finishing	Stores	Maintenance	Total	
15	Buildings insurance	Floor space (sq metres)	£3,300.00	£2,000.00	£600.00	£400.00	£200.00	£100.00	£3,300.00	OK
16	Depreciation of machinery	Value of machinery	£15,000.00	£8,750.00	£3,750.00	£1,250.00	£500.00	£750.00	£15,000.00	OK
17	Lighting and heating	Floor space (sq metres)	£9,900.00	£6,000.00	£1,800.00	£1,200.00	£600.00	£300.00	£9,900.00	OK
18	Rent and rates	Floor space (sq metres)	£19,965.00	£12,100.00	£3,630.00	£2,420.00	£1,210.00	£605.00	£19,965.00	OK
19	Supervisors' salaries	Number of employees	£39,600.00	£22,000.00	£8,800.00	£4,400.00	£2,200.00	£2,200.00	£39,600.00	OK
21			£87,765.00	£50,850.00	£18,580.00	£9,670.00	£4,710.00	£3,955.00	£87,765.00	£0.00
22	Stores			£2,826.00	£1,413.00	£471.00	-£4,400.00		£310.00	
23	Maintenance			£2,966.25	£593.25	£395.50		-£3,700.00	£255.00	
25	Total		£87,765.00	£56,642.25	£20,586.25	£10,536.50	£310.00	£255.00	£88,330.00	
27	OAR			£2.26	£5.33	£8.55				

Apportionment calculation / Basis of apportionment / Revised apportionment / Screen print

Task 2.2: 30 marks

(a)

	A	B	C	D	E	F	G	H	I	J	K
1	April sales					VAT	20%				
2	Transaction number	Product	Type	Colour	Gross amount	Net amount		177	Number of sales made in March		
3	90273	15cm Stoneware rectangular dish	Traditional	Slate	£15.00	£12.50					
4	90302	15cm Stoneware rectangular dish	Contemporary	Blackcurrant	£15.00	£12.50					
5	90318	30cm Stoneware fluted flan dish	Contemporary	Slate	£15.00	£12.50					
6	90339	30cm Stoneware fluted flan dish	Traditional	Leaf green	£15.00	£12.50					
7	90347	25cm Stoneware pie dish	Traditional	Blackcurrant	£15.00	£12.50					
8	90374	25cm Stoneware pie dish	Contemporary	Ivory	£15.00	£12.50					
9	90386	35cm Stoneware rectangular dish	Ornate	White	£15.00	£12.50					
10	90397	25cm Stoneware fluted flan dish	Traditional	Cherry	£15.00	£12.50					
11	90398	25cm Stoneware pie dish	Traditional	Sky blue	£15.00	£12.50					
12	90415	50cm Stoneware round platter	Traditional	Leaf green	£15.00	£12.50					
13	90287	25cm Stoneware pie dish	Traditional	Cherry	£20.00	£16.67					
14	90283	25cm Stoneware fluted flan dish	Traditional	Leaf green	£21.00	£17.50					
15	90331	20cm Stoneware rectangular dish	Contemporary	Cherry	£21.00	£17.50					
16	90354	35cm Stoneware rectangular dish	Contemporary	Sky blue	£21.00	£17.50					
17	90382	15cm Stoneware rectangular dish	Traditional	Blackcurrant	£21.00	£17.50					
18	90392	30cm Stoneware fluted flan dish	Contemporary	Sky blue	£21.00	£17.50					
19	90396	35cm Stoneware rectangular dish	Traditional	Blackcurrant	£21.00	£17.50					
20	90399	20cm Stoneware rectangular dish	Traditional	Leaf green	£21.00	£17.50					
21	90417	35cm Stoneware rectangular dish	Traditional	Slate	£21.00	£17.50					
22	90431	20cm Stoneware rectangular dish	Contemporary	Sky blue	£21.00	£17.50					
23	90274	35cm Stoneware rectangular dish	Contemporary	Slate	£22.00	£18.33					
24	90338	50cm Stoneware round platter	Ornate	Sky blue	£22.00	£18.33					
25	90345	15cm Stoneware rectangular dish	Contemporary	White	£22.00	£18.33					
26	90349	50cm Stoneware round platter	Traditional	Blackcurrant	£22.00	£18.33					
27	90435	25cm Stoneware fluted flan dish	Traditional	Leaf green	£26.00	£21.67					
28	90265	50cm Stoneware round platter	Traditional	Cherry	£32.00	£26.67					
29	90350	50cm Stoneware round platter	Contemporary	Blackcurrant	£34.00	£28.33					
30	90362	50cm Stoneware oval platter	Traditional	Sky blue	£34.00	£28.33					
31	90367	35cm Stoneware rectangular dish	Ornate	Slate	£34.00	£28.33					
32	90383	50cm Stoneware round platter	Ornate	Blackcurrant	£35.00	£29.17					
33	90410	25cm Stoneware pie dish	Contemporary	Cherry	£35.00	£29.17					
34	90412	50cm Stoneware oval platter	Contemporary	Sky blue	£35.00	£29.17					
35	90418	50cm Stoneware round platter	Traditional	Slate	£35.00	£29.17					
145	90303	30cm Stoneware fluted flan dish	Ornate	White	£115.00	£95.83					
146	90346	35cm Stoneware rectangular dish	Contemporary	Ivory	£120.00	£100.00					
147	90325	50cm Stoneware oval platter	Contemporary	Ivory	£123.00	£102.50					
148	90309	15cm Stoneware rectangular dish	Traditional	Sky blue	£134.00	£111.67					
149	90351	50cm Stoneware oval platter	Contemporary	Blackcurrant	£134.00	£111.67					
150	90368	50cm Stoneware round platter	Ornate	Slate	£134.00	£111.67					
151	90413	25cm Stoneware fluted flan dish	Traditional	Sky blue	£134.00	£111.67					
152	90384	25cm Stoneware fluted flan dish	Traditional	White	£162.00	£135.00					
153	90323	50cm Stoneware oval platter	Contemporary	White	£235.00	£195.83					
154	90359	25cm Stoneware fluted flan dish	Contemporary	White	£245.00	£204.17					
155	90285	35cm Stoneware rectangular dish	Traditional	Ivory	£325.00	£270.83					
156	90420	20cm Stoneware rectangular dish	Contemporary	Ivory	£345.00	£287.50					
157	90344	25cm Stoneware fluted flan dish	Contemporary	Ivory	£354.00	£295.00					
158	90304	25cm Stoneware pie dish	Traditional	White	£370.00	£308.33					
159	90389	50cm Stoneware round platter	Traditional	Ivory	£432.00	£360.00					
160	90371	25cm Stoneware pie dish	Ornate	White	£435.00	£362.50					
161	90305	15cm Stoneware rectangular dish	Ornate	Ivory	£452.00	£376.67					
162	90294	50cm Stoneware oval platter	Ornate	White	£554.00	£461.67					
163	90406	15cm Stoneware rectangular dish	Traditional	Ivory	£560.00	£466.67					
164	90387	20cm Stoneware rectangular dish	Traditional	Ivory	£674.00	£561.67					
165	90280	35cm Stoneware rectangular dish	Ornate	Ivory	£675.00	£562.50					
166	90336	20cm Stoneware rectangular dish	Ornate	Ivory	£675.00	£562.50					
167	90279	25cm Stoneware pie dish	Contemporary	White	£768.00	£640.00					
168	90324	25cm Stoneware fluted flan dish	Ornate	White	£778.00	£648.33					
169	90289	25cm Stoneware fluted flan dish	Ornate	Leaf green	£786.00	£655.00					
170	90334	20cm Stoneware rectangular dish	Ornate	Leaf green	£786.00	£655.00					
171	90337	35cm Stoneware rectangular dish	Traditional	Cherry	£786.00	£655.00					
172	90341	25cm Stoneware fluted flan dish	Contemporary	Slate	£786.00	£655.00					
173	90343	20cm Stoneware rectangular dish	Ornate	White	£786.00	£655.00					
174	90400	25cm Stoneware pie dish	Traditional	Leaf green	£786.00	£655.00					
175	90426	30cm Stoneware fluted flan dish	Traditional	Blackcurrant	£786.00	£655.00					
176	90278	30cm Stoneware fluted flan dish	Traditional	White	£829.00	£690.83					
177	90405	50cm Stoneware oval platter	Traditional	White	£987.00	£822.50					
178	90370	30cm Stoneware fluted flan dish	Contemporary	White	£1,111.00	£925.83					
179	90330	15cm Stoneware rectangular dish	Contemporary	Ivory	£1,205.00	£1,004.17					
180						£819.67	*Average of highest five sales*				
181											

Rows 36 to 145 are a continuation of the sorted sales.

(a) Formulas

	A	B	C	D	E	F	G	H
1	April sales					VAT	0.2	
2	Transaction number	Product	Type	Colour	Gross amount	Net amount		=COUNT(F3:F179)
3	90273	15cm Stoneware rectangular dish	Traditional	Slate	15	=E3/(1+$G$1)		
4	90302	15cm Stoneware rectangular dish	Contemporary	Blackcurrant	15	=E4/(1+$G$1)		
5	90318	30cm Stoneware fluted flan dish	Contemporary	Slate	15	=E5/(1+$G$1)		Number of sales made in March
6	90339	30cm Stoneware fluted flan dish	Traditional	Leaf green	15	=E6/(1+$G$1)		
7	90347	25cm Stoneware pie dish	Traditional	Blackcurrant	15	=E7/(1+$G$1)		
8	90374	25cm Stoneware pie dish	Contemporary	Ivory	15	=E8/(1+$G$1)		
9	90386	35cm Stoneware rectangular dish	Ornate	White	15	=E9/(1+$G$1)		
10	90397	25cm Stoneware fluted flan dish	Traditional	Cherry	15	=E10/(1+$G$1)		
11	90398	25cm Stoneware pie dish	Traditional	Sky blue	15	=E11/(1+$G$1)		
12	90415	50cm Stoneware round platter	Traditional	Leaf green	15	=E12/(1+$G$1)		
13	90287	25cm Stoneware pie dish	Traditional	Cherry	20	=E13/(1+$G$1)		
14	90283	25cm Stoneware fluted flan dish	Traditional	Leaf green	21	=E14/(1+$G$1)		
15	90331	20cm Stoneware rectangular dish	Contemporary	Cherry	21	=E15/(1+$G$1)		
16	90354	35cm Stoneware rectangular dish	Contemporary	Sky blue	21	=E16/(1+$G$1)		
17	90382	15cm Stoneware rectangular dish	Traditional	Blackcurrant	21	=E17/(1+$G$1)		
170	90334	20cm Stoneware rectangular dish	Ornate	Leaf green	786	=E170/(1+$G$1)		
171	90337	35cm Stoneware rectangular dish	Traditional	Cherry	786	=E171/(1+$G$1)		
172	90341	25cm Stoneware fluted flan dish	Contemporary	Slate	786	=E172/(1+$G$1)		
173	90343	20cm Stoneware rectangular dish	Ornate	White	786	=E173/(1+$G$1)		
174	90400	25cm Stoneware pie dish	Traditional	Leaf green	786	=E174/(1+$G$1)		
175	90426	30cm Stoneware fluted flan dish	Traditional	Blackcurrant	786	=E175/(1+$G$1)		
176	90278	30cm Stoneware fluted flan dish	Traditional	White	829	=E176/(1+$G$1)		
177	90405	50cm Stoneware oval platter	Traditional	White	987	=E177/(1+$G$1)		
178	90370	30cm Stoneware fluted flan dish	Contemporary	White	1111	=E178/(1+$G$1)		
179	90330	15cm Stoneware rectangular dish	Contemporary	Ivory	1205	=E179/(1+$G$1)		
180						=AVERAGE(F175:F179)	Average of highest five sales	
181								
182								

Traditional Range Sales / Stoneware sales March / Formulas / Capital account / Forecast sales commission / Goal seek

Rows 18 to 169 are a continuation of the formulas where the data has been sorted by the net amount.

(b)

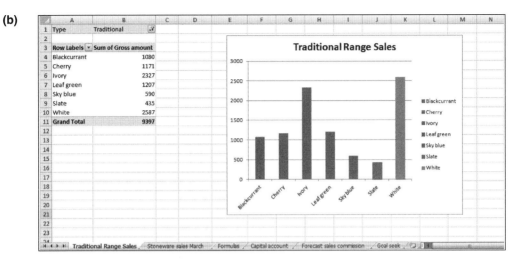

(b) pdf file 'Practice Assessment 3 Task 2.2 Traditional Sales Range Chart'

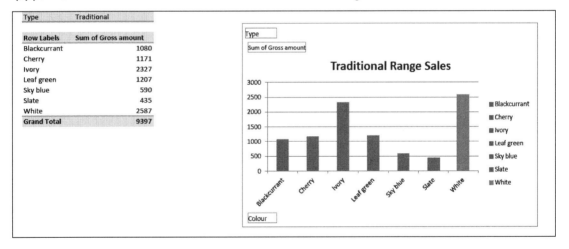

Type	Traditional
Row Labels	**Sum of Gross amount**
Blackcurrant	1080
Cherry	1171
Ivory	2327
Leaf green	1207
Sky blue	590
Slate	435
White	2587
Grand Total	**9397**

(c)

	A	B	C	D	E	F	G	H	I
1	Beautiful Tableware Capital Statements								
2			Claire	Jason	Andrea	Total			
3									
4	1 April 20X5	Initial capital	£35,000	£25,000	£0	£60,000			
5	1 April 20X5	Goodwill created	£28,800	£19,200	£0	£48,000			
6	1 April 20X5	Goodwill written off	-£18,000	-£12,000	-£18,000	-£48,000			
7	1 April 20X5	Additional capital			£45,000	£45,000			
8	1 April 20X5	Revised capital	£45,800	£32,200	£27,000	£105,000			
9									
10									
11									
12									
13									
14									
15									
16									
17									

Traditional Range Sales / Stoneware sales March / Formulas / Capital account / Forecast sales commission / Goal seek

(d)

	A	B	C	D	E
1	Commission %	5%			
2	Minimum monthly sales	£8,000			
3					
4	Sales and rebate for year ended 31 December 20X8				
5		Sales		Commission	
6	Month	Claire	Jason	Claire	Jason
7	January	£6,795.00	£3,567.00	£0.00	£0.00
8	February	£18,765.00	£2,453.00	£938.25	£0.00
9	March	£2,346.00	£2,654.00	£0.00	£0.00
10	April	£5,609.00	£9,076.00	£0.00	£453.80
11	May	£4,320.00	£4,964.00	£0.00	£0.00
12	June	£11,212.00	£8,709.00	£560.60	£435.45
13	July	£9,765.00	£12,500.00	£488.25	£625.00
14	August	£5,486.00	£9,801.00	£0.00	£490.05
15	September	£18,750.00	£21,760.00	£937.50	£1,088.00
16	October	£6,398.00	£9,650.00	£0.00	£482.50
17	November	£14,600.00	£18,042.00	£730.00	£902.10
18	December	£12,063.00	£12,960.00	£603.15	£648.00
19		£116,109.00	£116,136.00	£4,257.75	£5,124.90
20					

(e) Showing Goal Seek formula

	A	B	C	D	E	F	G	H
1	Commission %	5%						
2	Minimum monthly sales	£8,000						
3								
4	Sales and rebate for year ended 31 December 20X8							
5		Sales		Commission				
6	Month	Claire	Jason	Claire	Jason			
7	January	£6,795.00	£3,567.00	£0.00	£0.00			
8	February	£18,765.00	£2,453.00	£938.25	£0.00			
9	March	£2,346.00	£2,654.00	£0.00	£0.00			
10	April	£5,609.00	£9,076.00	£0.00	£453.80			
11	May	£4,320.00	£4,964.00	£0.00	£0.00			
12	June	£11,212.00	£8,709.00	£560.60	£435.45			
13	July	£9,765.00	£12,500.00	£488.25	£625.00			
14	August	£5,486.00	£9,801.00	£0.00	£490.05			
15	September	£18,750.00	£21,760.00	£937.50	£1,088.00			
16	October	£6,398.00	£9,650.00	£0.00	£482.50			
17	November	£14,600.00	£18,042.00	£730.00	£902.10			
18	December	£12,063.00	£12,960.00	£603.15	£648.00			
19		£116,109.00	£116,136.00	£4,257.75	£5,124.90			
20								
21								

Goal Seek dialog box:
- Set cell: $D$19
- To value: 7000
- By changing cell: $B$1
- OK   Cancel

Sheet tabs: Stoneware sales March / Formulas / Capital account / Forecast sales commission / Goal seek

(e) Showing results of Goal Seek

	A	B	C	D	E	F
1	Commission %	8%				
2	Minimum monthly sales	£8,000				
3						
4	Sales and rebate for year ended 31 December 20X8					
5		Sales		Commission		
6	Month	Claire	Jason	Claire	Jason	
7	January	£6,795.00	£3,567.00	£0.00	£0.00	
8	February	£18,765.00	£2,453.00	£1,542.54	£0.00	
9	March	£2,346.00	£2,654.00	£0.00	£0.00	
10	April	£5,609.00	£9,076.00	£0.00	£746.07	
11	May	£4,320.00	£4,964.00	£0.00	£0.00	
12	June	£11,212.00	£8,709.00	£921.66	£715.91	
13	July	£9,765.00	£12,500.00	£802.71	£1,027.54	
14	August	£5,486.00	£9,801.00	£0.00	£805.67	
15	September	£18,750.00	£21,760.00	£1,541.31	£1,788.74	
16	October	£6,398.00	£9,650.00	£0.00	£793.26	
17	November	£14,600.00	£18,042.00	£1,200.16	£1,483.11	
18	December	£12,063.00	£12,960.00	£991.62	£1,065.35	
19		£116,109.00	£116,136.00	£7,000.00	£8,425.65	
20						
21						

Answers to practice synoptic assessment 4

Section 1

Task 1.1: 15 marks

(a)

Statement	True	False
Galvanised Products Limited's reputation may be damaged if I do not comply with the Code of Ethics	✔	
The Code of Ethics sets out the rules I must apply in my work and personal life		✔

(b)

Situation	Comply	Not Comply
Edyta informs her manager she is sick, when she is, in fact, going away for a long weekend		✔
Edyta made an error on payroll. She knows the incorrect information is included in the monthly reporting		✔

(c)   (a)   Integrity

The sales bonuses are not fair and are no longer being given transparently.

(d)   (b)   A self-interest threat

Action	Tick to do
Request the Finance Director review the provision for bad and doubtful debts	✔
Follow the provisioning policy, as set out by the Finance Director	✔
Request to be removed from the work for this year end	✔

(e)

Action	
(a) Discuss the matter with the management of Galvanised Products Limited and request they comply with the health and safety regulations	✔
(b) Resign	
(c) Report Galvanised Products Limited to the Health and Safety Executive immediately	

(f)

Action	
(a) Tell the Purchasing Director to stop	
(b) Inform the Managing Director of the Purchasing Director's actions	✔

(g) Paul must **phone the AAT's Confidential helpline** to determine what to do next. If he believes the directors will destroy evidence of the bribes, he must make **a protected disclosure** to the relevant authority.

Task 1.2: 15 marks

(a) £5373

(b) The VAT amount will be **due to** HMRC.

(c) (b) The principle of materiality means that the users' view of the accounts will not change if small items, such as clothes hangers, are not capitalised

(d) (c) The financial statements need to be free from material misstatement

(e) £1,750 + £8,470 + (£3,090/3) = £11,250

(f) £4,200 – £500 – £256 = £3,444

(g) (a) Discuss this transaction with Luke Graham to find out if it is an error

(h) (a) Explain that you have no experience of doing this to Luke and refuse to do it
(b) Suggest Luke discuss this with his accountant
(c) Contact the AAT helpline

Task 1.3: 15 marks

(a)   Luke's treatment of the suppliers is against the principle of long-term sustainability, as some suppliers may face cash flow and profitability pressures by agreeing to these requests. His request could be detrimental to the long-term prosperity of his business, should he be unable to obtain appropriate quality supplies.

Ethically he should pay a fair price for the goods he purchases and pay for goods on time. By imposing a discount and extending credit terms without consultation and for no reason, he is not behaving in a sustainable manner.

(b)   **Threat 1**

I am facing a self-interest threat to my objectivity, as my fees rely on supporting Luke in this unethical, unsustainable behaviour.

Threat 2

I am also facing an intimidation threat because Luke is suggesting he will find another bookkeeper, so I will lose his fee income.

(c)   I can tell Luke that he is acting unethically and suggest he consider the long-term implications of his actions. I can tell him I will not help him to persuade the suppliers to comply with his request.

If Luke continues to implement his new policy, I may need to resign as his bookkeeper.

(d)

EMAIL

To: Luke Graham

From: Bruno Costa

Date: 30 June 20-6

Subject: Partnership vs sole trader

Hello Luke

Thank you for your email dated 30 June 20-6.

(1) Partnerships are formed between two or more people, whereas a sole trader is just you, continuing to trade as you are.

(2) A partnership will either be governed by an agreement you draw up with your partner or, if there is no agreement, by the Partnership Act 1890.

There will be another person to assist in managing the business, to give continuity for holidays or sickness.

Each partner will be liable for the debts of the whole business, unless it is set up as a Limited Liability Partnership. As a sole trader you are currently just responsible for the transactions you enter into yourself.

In a partnership, you will have an agreed share of the profits and will pay income tax on this amount. As a sole trader you are taxed on all the profits of the business.

(3) One advantage would be that you have access to the additional capital you want to expand your business.

One disadvantage would be that you would be liable for any decisions made for the business by your partner.

Please contact me if you require any further information.

Best wishes

Bruno

Section 2

Task 2.1: 25 marks

(a) – (d)

	A	B	C	D	E
1	**Trendy Togs**				
2	**Break-even analysis new shop**				
3		£			
4					
5	Staff (2 people)	36,000			
6	Electricity	6,300			
7	Depreciation on shop fitting/ equipment	5,000			
8	Rent	22,000			
9	Rates	3,150			
10	Phone (fixed contract)	500			
11	Administration	5,000			
12	Insurance	1,100			
13	Marketing	2,000			
14					
15		81,050			
16					
17	**Break-even analysis new shop**				
18		**Break-even**	**Target profit**	**Target profit**	
19			£75,000	£50,000	
20					
21	Fixed Costs	£81,050	£81,050	£81,050	
22					
23	Revenue Required	£162,100	£312,100	£262,100	
24					
25					
26					
27	**Bonus calculation**	Revenue	Bonus		
28					
29	Bonus payable	£ 160,000	No bonus		
30	Bonus payable	£ 300,000	£ 2,069		
31	Bonus payable	£ 400,000	£ 3,569		
32					
33					

Coffee and cake data | **Break-even analysis** | Screen print

(a) – (d) showing formulas

	A	B	C	D	E
1	Trendy Togs				
2	Break-even analysis new shop				
3		£			
4					
5	Staff (2 people)	=+'Coffee and cake data'!B4/1.5 *2			
6	Electricity	=+'Coffee and cake data'!B5*1.05			
7	Depreciation on shop fitting/ equipment	5000			
8	Rent	=+'Coffee and cake data'!B7*1.1			
9	Rates	=+'Coffee and cake data'!B8*1.05			
10	Phone (fixed contract)	=+'Coffee and cake data'!B9			
11	Administration	=+'Coffee and cake data'!B10			
12	Insurance	=+'Coffee and cake data'!B11*1.1			
13	Marketing	=+'Coffee and cake data'!B12			
14					
15		=SUM(B5:B14)			
16					
17		Break-even analysis new shop			
18		Break-even	Target profit 75000	Target profit 50000	
19					
20					
21	Fixed Costs	=+B15	=+B15	=+B15	
22					
23	Revenue Required	=+B21/0.5	=+(C21+C19)/0.5	=+(D21+D19)/0.5	
24					
25					
26					
27	Bonus calculation	Revenue	Bonus		
28					
29	Bonus payable	160000	=IF(B29>B$23,(B29-B$23)*0.015,"No bonus")		
30	Bonus payable	300000	=IF(B30>B$23,(B30-B$23)*0.015,"No bonus")		
31	Bonus payable	400000	=IF(B31>B$23,(B31-B$23)*0.015,"No bonus")		
32					
33					

Coffee and cake data ⟋ Break-even analysis ⟋ Screen print

Task 2.2: 30 marks

(a) and (c)

	A	B	C	D	E	F	G	H	I	J	K
1	Sales Data June						2				
2	Trendy Togs										
3											
4	Invoice number	Customer	Type	Gross	VAT rate	Net					
5	3425	Andrews	Children	£187.60	0%	£187.60					
6	3430	Attire	Children	£121.15	0%	£121.15					
7	3463	Andrews	Children	£203.70	0%	£203.70					
8	3434	Fine Fashion	Children	£107.90	0%	£107.90					
9	3439	Attitude	Children	£134.84	0%	£134.84					
10	3469	Andrews	Children	£203.20	0%	£203.20					
11	3446	Attire	Children	£62.25	0%	£62.25					
12	3473	Andrews	Children	£33.60	0%	£33.60					
13	3450	Fine Fashion	Children	£29.70	0%	£29.70					
14	3454	Attire	Children	£85.00	0%	£85.00					
15	3478	Andrews	Children	£85.20	0%	£85.20					
16	3458	Fine Fashion	Children	£40.00	0%	£40.00					
17	3481	Arnold & Co	Children	£81.12	0%	£81.12					
18	3488	Arnold & Co	Children	£56.02	0%	£56.02					
19	3492	Fine Fashion	Children	£26.73	0%	£26.73					
20	3497	Men & Women	Children	£108.72	0%	£108.72					
80	3480	Men & Women	Women	£284.80	20%	£237.33					
81	3484	Attitude	Women	£229.16	20%	£190.97					
82	3449	Andrews	Women	£139.40	20%	£116.17					
83	3486	Fine Fashion	Women	£306.94	20%	£255.78					
84	3487	Men & Women	Women	£121.99	20%	£101.66					
85	3457	Andrews	Women	£106.50	20%	£88.75					
86	3472	Andrews	Women	£166.40	20%	£138.67					
87	3496	Fine Fashion	Women	£76.50	20%	£63.75					
88	3491	Andrews	Women	£125.46	20%	£104.55					
89	3501	Men & Women	Women	£320.40	20%	£267.00					
90	3503	Bladons	Women	£252.85	20%	£210.71					
91	3495	Andrews	Women	£26.73	20%	£22.28					
92	3507	Fine Fashion	Women	£375.15	20%	£312.63					
93	3512	Andrews	Women	£153.34	20%	£127.78					
94											
95			Maximum sales value			£822.50					
96			Minimum sales value			£19.80					
97											
98											

Analysis Andrews   Invoices   VAT Information   Extended Trial Balance   Missing Inventory information   Screen print   Formulas ETB

Rows 21 to 79 are a continuation of the data sorted by the type of sale.

(a) and (c) showing formulas

	A	B	C	D	E	F	G
1	Sales Data June						
2	Trendy Togs						
3							
4	Invoice number	Customer	Type	Gross	VAT rate	Net	2
5	3425	Andrews	Children	187.6	=VLOOKUP(C5,'VAT Information'!$A$3:$B$5,2, FALSE)	=D5/(1+E5)	
6	3430	Attire	Children	121.15	=VLOOKUP(C6,'VAT Information'!$A$3:$B$5,2, FALSE)	=D6/(1+E6)	
7	3463	Andrews	Children	203.7	=VLOOKUP(C7,'VAT Information'!$A$3:$B$5,2, FALSE)	=D7/(1+E7)	
8	3434	Fine Fashion	Children	107.9	=VLOOKUP(C8,'VAT Information'!$A$3:$B$5,2, FALSE)	=D8/(1+E8)	
9	3439	Attitude	Children	134.84	=VLOOKUP(C9,'VAT Information'!$A$3:$B$5,2, FALSE)	=D9/(1+E9)	
10	3469	Andrews	Children	203.2	=VLOOKUP(C10,'VAT Information'!$A$3:$B$5,2, FALSE)	=D10/(1+E10)	
11	3446	Attire	Children	62.25	=VLOOKUP(C11,'VAT Information'!$A$3:$B$5,2, FALSE)	=D11/(1+E11)	
12	3473	Andrews	Children	33.6	=VLOOKUP(C12,'VAT Information'!$A$3:$B$5,2, FALSE)	=D12/(1+E12)	
13	3450	Fine Fashion	Children	29.7	=VLOOKUP(C13,'VAT Information'!$A$3:$B$5,2, FALSE)	=D13/(1+E13)	
14	3454	Attire	Children	85	=VLOOKUP(C14,'VAT Information'!$A$3:$B$5,2, FALSE)	=D14/(1+E14)	
15	3478	Andrews	Children	85.2	=VLOOKUP(C15,'VAT Information'!$A$3:$B$5,2, FALSE)	=D15/(1+E15)	
16	3458	Fine Fashion	Children	40	=VLOOKUP(C16,'VAT Information'!$A$3:$B$5,2, FALSE)	=D16/(1+E16)	
17	3481	Arnold & Co	Children	81.12	=VLOOKUP(C17,'VAT Information'!$A$3:$B$5,2, FALSE)	=D17/(1+E17)	
18	3488	Arnold & Co	Children	56.02	=VLOOKUP(C18,'VAT Information'!$A$3:$B$5,2, FALSE)	=D18/(1+E18)	
19	3492	Fine Fashion	Children	26.73	=VLOOKUP(C19,'VAT Information'!$A$3:$B$5,2, FALSE)	=D19/(1+E19)	
20	3497	Men & Women	Children	108.72	=VLOOKUP(C20,'VAT Information'!$A$3:$B$5,2, FALSE)	=D20/(1+E20)	
81	3484	Attitude	Women	229.16	=VLOOKUP(C81,'VAT Information'!$A$3:$B$5,2, FALSE)	=D81/(1+E81)	
82	3449	Andrews	Women	139.4	=VLOOKUP(C82,'VAT Information'!$A$3:$B$5,2, FALSE)	=D82/(1+E82)	
83	3486	Fine Fashion	Women	306.94	=VLOOKUP(C83,'VAT Information'!$A$3:$B$5,2, FALSE)	=D83/(1+E83)	
84	3487	Men & Women	Women	121.99	=VLOOKUP(C84,'VAT Information'!$A$3:$B$5,2, FALSE)	=D84/(1+E84)	
85	3457	Andrews	Women	106.5	=VLOOKUP(C85,'VAT Information'!$A$3:$B$5,2, FALSE)	=D85/(1+E85)	
86	3472	Andrews	Women	166.4	=VLOOKUP(C86,'VAT Information'!$A$3:$B$5,2, FALSE)	=D86/(1+E86)	
87	3496	Fine Fashion	Women	76.5	=VLOOKUP(C87,'VAT Information'!$A$3:$B$5,2, FALSE)	=D87/(1+E87)	
88	3491	Andrews	Women	125.46	=VLOOKUP(C88,'VAT Information'!$A$3:$B$5,2, FALSE)	=D88/(1+E88)	
89	3501	Men & Women	Women	320.4	=VLOOKUP(C89,'VAT Information'!$A$3:$B$5,2, FALSE)	=D89/(1+E89)	
90	3503	Bladons	Women	252.85	=VLOOKUP(C90,'VAT Information'!$A$3:$B$5,2, FALSE)	=D90/(1+E90)	
91	3495	Andrews	Women	26.73	=VLOOKUP(C91,'VAT Information'!$A$3:$B$5,2, FALSE)	=D91/(1+E91)	
92	3507	Fine Fashion	Women	375.15	=VLOOKUP(C92,'VAT Information'!$A$3:$B$5,2, FALSE)	=D92/(1+E92)	
93	3512	Andrews	Women	153.34	=VLOOKUP(C93,'VAT Information'!$A$3:$B$5,2, FALSE)	=D93/(1+E93)	
94							
95		Maximum sales value				=MAX(F5:F93)	
96		Minimum sales value				=MIN(F5:F93)	
97							
98							
99							
100							

Analysis Andrews | Invoices | VAT Information | Extended Trial Balance | Missing inventory information | Screen print | Formulas ETB

Rows 21 to 80 are a continuation of the data sorted by the type of sale.

(b)

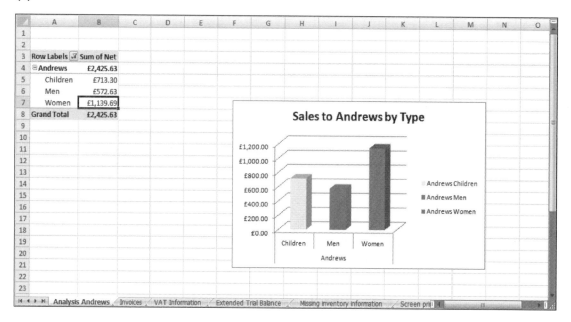

(d) and (f)

Trendy Togs

EXTENDED TRIAL BALANCE AS AT 31 MARCH 20X6

	Ledger Balances DR	Ledger Balances CR	Adjustments DR	Adjustments CR	Statement of profit or loss DR	Statement of profit or loss CR	Statement of financial position DR	Statement of financial position CR
Opening inventory	6000				6000			
Purchases	71435				71435			
Bank	25990						25990	
Cash	231						231	
Sales ledger control account	22165						22165	
Prepayments	545						545	
Van at cost	15000						15000	
Fixtures and fittings at cost	12600						12600	
Depreciation van		12000		2000				14000
Depreciation fixtures and fittings		6300		1260				7560
Value Added Tax		14598						14598
Purchases ledger control		17912						17912
Accruals		4500						4500
Capital		22600						22600
Drawings	24100						24100	
Sales revenue		135897				135897		
Rent	11250				11250			
Interest paid	300				300			
Telephone	1050				1050			
Light Heat	2789				2789			
Wages	14033				14033			
Insurance	753				753			
Vehicle costs	3444				3444			
Marketing	780				780			
Other expenses	1342				1342			
Allowance for doubtful debts				222				222
Allowance for doubtful debts : adjustment			222		222			
Depreciation			3260		3260			
Closing inventory Statement of profit or loss				8492		8492		
Closing inventory Statement of financial position			8492				8492	
Profit/loss for the year					27731			27731
Totals	213807	213807	3482	3482	144389	144389	109123	109123
	OK		OK		OK		OK	

Analysis Andrews Invoices VAT Information Extended Trial Balance Missing inventory information Screen print

Formulas columns E – H

Trendy Togs

EXTENDED TRIAL BALANCE AS AT 31 MARCH 20X6

	Ledger Balances		Adjustments	
	DR	CR	DR	CR
Opening inventory	6000			
Purchases	71435			
Bank	25990			
Cash	231			
Sales ledger control account	22165			
Prepayments	545			
Van at cost	15000			
Fixtures and fittings at cost	12600			
Depreciation van		12000	2000	
Depreciation fixtures and fittings		6300	1260	
Value Added Tax		14598		
Purchases ledger control		17912		
Accruals		4500		
Capital		22600		
Drawings	24100			
Sales revenue		135897		
Rent	11250			
Interest paid	300			
Telephone	1050			
Light Heat	2789			
Wages	14033			
Insurance	753			
Vehicle costs	3444			
Marketing	780			
Other expenses	1342			
Allowance for doubtful debts				
Allowance for doubtful debts ; adjustment			=ROUND(+E8*0.01,0)	=ROUND(+E8*0.01,0)
Depreciation			=2000+1260	
Closing inventory Statement of profit or loss				
Closing inventory Statement of financial position				
Profit/loss for the year				
Totals	=SUM(E4:E34)	=SUM(F4:F34)	=SUM(G4:G34)	=SUM(H4:H34)
		=IF(E35-F35=0,"OK",E35-F35)		=IF(G35-H35=0,"OK",G35-H35)

Analysis Andrews   Invoices   VAT Information   Extended Trial Balance   Missing inventory information   Screen print   Formulas ETB

Formulas columns I – L

	I	J	K	L
Trendy Togs				
EXTENDED TRIAL BALANCE AS AT 31 MARCH 20X6	Statement of profit or loss		Statement of financial position	
	DR	CR	DR	CR
Opening inventory	=+E4+G4-H4			
Purchases	=+E5+G5-H5			
Bank			=+E6+G6-H6	
Cash			=+E7+G7-H7	
Sales ledger control account			=+E8+G8-H8	
Prepayments			=+E9+G9-H9	
Van at cost			=+E10+G10-H10	
Fixtures and fittings at cost			=+E11+G11-H11	
Depreciation van				=+F12+H12-G12
Depreciation fixtures and fittings				=+F13+H13-G13
Value Added Tax				=+F14+H14-G14
Purchases ledger control				=+F15+H15-G15
Accruals				=+F16+H16-G16
Capital				=+F17+H17-G17
Drawings			=+E18+G18+H18	
Sales revenue		=+F19+H19-G19		
Rent	=+E20+G20-H20			
Interest paid	=+E21+G21-H21			
Telephone	=+E22+G22-H22			
Light Heat	=+E23+G23-H23			
Wages	=+E24+G24-H24			
Insurance	=+E25+G25-H25			
Vehicle costs	=+E26+G26-H26			
Marketing	=+E27+G27-H27			
Other expenses	=+E28+G28-H28			
Allowance for doubtful debts				=+H29
Allowance for doubtful debts : adjustment	=+G30			
Depreciation	=+E31+G31-H31			
Closing inventory Statement of profit or loss		='Missing inventory information'!F20		
Closing inventory Statement of financial position			='Missing inventory information'!F20	
Profit/loss for the year	=SUM(J4:J33)-SUM(I4:I32)			=I34
Totals	=SUM(I4:I34)	=SUM(J4:J34)	=SUM(K4:K34)	=SUM(L4:L34)
		=IF(I35-J35=0,"OK",I35-J35)		=IF(K35-L35=0,"OK",K35-L35)

Analysis Andrews | Invoices | VAT Information | Extended Trial Balance | Missing inventory information | Screen print

(e)

	A	B	C	D	E	F	G	H
1	Year ended 31 March 20X6							
2	Current closing inventory valuation					£6,702		
3								
4	Box of inventory items							
5	Inventory nu	Description	Quantity	Cost per item	NRV per item	Inventory valuation		
6	21409	Children's dresses	7	£25	£35	£175		
7	21908	Women's dresses	4	£30	£25	£100		
8	23721	Women's dresses	3	£45	£65	£135		
9	35665	Children's dresses	10	£23	£19	£190		
10	42671	Men's shirt	12	£30	£20	£240		
11	43768	Men's trousers	3	£35	£50	£105		
12	43789	Men's trousers	7	£25	£30	£175		
13	56342	Women's trousers	3	£25	£20	£60		
14	65290	Children's tops	1	£5	£10	£5		
15	76301	Men's trousers	5	£32	£22	£110		
16	76890	Men's shirt	10	£35	£65	£350		
17	98573	Women's trousers	5	£29	£45	£145		
18					*Total*	*£1,790*		
19								
20	Revised closing inventory valuation					£8,492		
21								
22								
23								
24								
25								

Analysis Andrews / Invoices / VAT Information / Extended Trial Balance / **Missing inventory information** / Screen print / Formulas ETB

(e) showing formulas

	A	B	C	D	E	F
1	Year ended 31 March 20X6					
2	Current closing inventory valuation					6702
3						
4	Box of inventory items					
5	Inventory number	Description	Quantity	Cost per item	NRV per item	Inventory valuation
6	21409	Children's dresses	7	25	35	=IF(D6<E6,+C6*D6, E6*C6)
7	21908	Women's dresses	4	30	25	=IF(D7<E7,+C7*D7, E7*C7)
8	23721	Women's dresses	3	45	65	=IF(D8<E8,+C8*D8, E8*C8)
9	35665	Children's dresses	10	23	19	=IF(D9<E9,+C9*D9, E9*C9)
10	42671	Men's shirt	12	30	20	=IF(D10<E10,+C10*D10, E10*C10)
11	43768	Men's trousers	3	35	50	=IF(D11<E11,+C11*D11, E11*C11)
12	43789	Men's trousers	7	25	30	=IF(D12<E12,+C12*D12, E12*C12)
13	56342	Women's trousers	3	25	20	=IF(D13<E13,+C13*D13, E13*C13)
14	65290	Children's tops	1	5	10	=IF(D14<E14,+C14*D14, E14*C14)
15	76301	Men's trousers	5	32	22	=IF(D15<E15,+C15*D15, E15*C15)
16	76890	Men's shirt	10	35	65	=IF(D16<E16,+C16*D16, E16*C16)
17	98573	Women's trousers	5	29	45	=IF(D17<E17,+C17*D17, E17*C17)
18					*Total*	=SUM(F6:F17)
19						
20	Revised closing inventory valuation					=+F18+F2
21						
22						
23						
24						
25						

Analysis Andrews / Invoices / VAT Information / Extended Trial Balance / **Missing inventory information** / Screen print / Formulas ETB

for your notes

for your notes

for your notes

for your notes

for your notes

for your notes

for your notes

for your notes

for your notes

for your notes